# Table of Contents

## Unit 1 Sentence Structure

### Looking  Back Communities Long Ago

## Unit 2 Parts of Speech

### Unforgettable Folks Inventors

## Unit 3 Usage

### Grab Bag Games and Activities

## Unit 4 Grammar

### Beasts & Critters Endangered Animals

# Unit 5 Mechanics

## The World Outside Nature's Extremes

## Unit Assessments

## Extra Practice

## Unit Tests

## G.U.M. Handbook

## G.U.M. Indexes

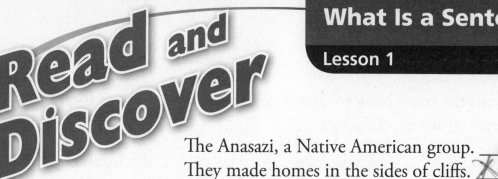

# Read and Discover

The Anasazi, a Native American group. ____
They made homes in the sides of cliffs. ✗

**Write *X* next to the group of words that makes sense and tells a complete thought.**

A **simple sentence** is a group of words that tells one complete thought. One part of a sentence tells whom or what the sentence is about. The other part tells what happened. A sentence begins with a capital letter and ends with an end mark.

See Handbook **Sections 1, 6, and 9**

# Part 1

Write *S* next to each complete sentence.

1. The Anasazi lived in the New Mexico area. ___

2. Nine hundred years ago. ____

3. Large homes high on the sides of cliffs. ____

4. One house had 225 rooms. ____

5. Climbed ladders up to their homes. ____

6. Crops cannot grow on cliffs. ____

7. The Anasazi grew corn on the mesa above or in the valley below. ____

8. About 700 years ago all the Anasazi left their cliff homes. ____

9. Clues to the Anasazi's way of life. ____

10. Scientists have many questions about these cliff dwellers. ____

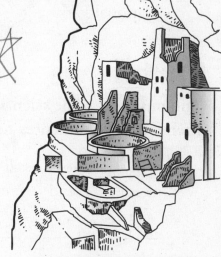

**The Anasazi cliff houses were like apartment buildings built into the rocks.**

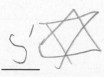

# Part 2

Write a phrase from the word bank to complete each sentence. Don't forget to begin each sentence with a capital letter.

| scientists | many homes | the Anasazi people ✓ |
| had many rooms ✓ | climbed ladders to their homes ✓ | |

11. The Anasazi people ✓ _____ lived in the cliffs.

12. Their homes __Had many rooms✓__ .

13. The Anasazi __climbed ladders to there homes__✓ .

14. ___Scientists✓___ have found many clues about the Anasazi.

15. ___Many homes✓___ are built into the cliffs at Mesa Verde National Park.

# Part 3

Find out what some scientists think about the Anasazi. Unscramble the sentences. Then write the sentences to answer the questions.

16. Why did the Anasazi build their homes in the sides of cliffs?
them.    could    enemies    Their    not    attack
__Their enemies could not attack The__

17. Why did the Anasazi leave their cliff homes? Write two reasons.
The    drier.    much    became    climate
__The climat becam drier__

for    grow    They    not    food    could    themselves.
__They could not grow food for Themselfs__

Looking Back

Ghost towns are found in many states.

Circle the part of the sentence that tells what the sentence is about.

The **subject** is the part of the sentence that tells whom or what the sentence is about. The subject can be one or more words. The subject is usually at the beginning of a sentence.

See Handbook **Section 10**

# Part 1

Draw a box around the subject of each sentence.

1. Bodie was a big town once.

2. W.S. Bodey discovered gold there in 1859.

3. Many people moved there because of the gold.

4. A few miners earned a lot of money.

5. Bodie has very hot weather in the summer.

6. Winter brings snow and bitter cold.

7. Few people enjoyed life in Bodie.

8. Gold lost most of its value in the 1930s.

9. Almost everyone left town after that.

10. Many empty cabins stand on the dusty streets of Bodie today.

**WELCOME TO BODIE POPULATION 10,000**

**In 1880 Bodie, California, had about as many residents as Los Angeles.**

# Part 2

Imagine that you visit Bodie. Add a subject to each sentence to tell what you might see or hear. You can use words in the word bank if you like. Don't forget to begin each sentence with a capital letter.

| lizard | wagons | coyotes ✓ | jackrabbit |
|--------|--------|-----------|------------|
| doors ✓ | windows ✓ | tumbleweeds ✓ | dust |

11. ___Tumbleweeds___ ✓ blew down the street.

12. ___Windows___ were broken long ago.

13. ___Door___ creaked in the wind.

14. ___Coyotes___ howled in the hills.

15. ___Jack rabits___ sat in the middle of the street.

# Part 3

Draw a line to match each subject with a group of words that makes sense. (The subjects are underlined.) You can make three sentences.

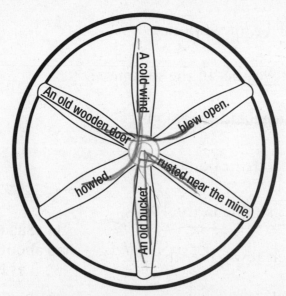

Name _____

Looking Back

English colonists/settled on an island off North Carolina.

**Underline the part of the sentence that tells what the subject did.**

The **predicate** is the part of the sentence that tells what the subject is or does.

See Handbook  Section 11

## Part 1

Draw a line under the predicate in each sentence.

1. Settlers arrived on Roanoke Island in 1585.

2. The colonists had very little food.

3. They sailed back to England a year later.

4. A second group arrived there in 1587.

5. John White led the group of men, women, and children.

6. He sailed back to England after a while for more supplies.

7. A war delayed his return to the colony.

8. He found a terrible surprise upon his return.

9. No colonists remained on the island.

10. Only a single carved word gave a clue.

# Part 2

Think about the clue that John White found and what it could mean. Write a predicate from the word bank to complete each sentence. Remember to end each sentence with a period.

| | | |
|---|---|---|
| were torn down | said Croatoan | had this name |
| found no other clues | may have joined a Native American tribe | |

11. The carving _____

12. A native people _____

13. John White _____

14. The houses _____

15. The colonists _____

# Part 3

See Handbook  Section 30

Ask an adult to help you search the Internet for information about what Roanoke Island is like today. Draw a picture of it. Write a complete sentence about it. Draw a line under the predicate.

_____

_____

Name _____

**Looking Back**

# Read and Discover

Pompeii was an ancient Roman city. _____
What happened there? _____

**Put a check by the sentence that asks a question.
Circle the punctuation mark the question ends with.**

A **telling sentence** makes a statement. It ends with a period. An **asking sentence** asks a question. It ends with a question mark. Both types of sentence begin with a capital letter.

See Handbook Sections 6 and 9

# Part 1

Write *A* next to each asking sentence and *T* next to each telling sentence. Circle each end mark.

1. There was a volcano near Pompeii. _____

2. Did the volcano erupt? _____

3. The volcano buried the city in ash. _____

4. Was the blast loud? _____

5. What is left in Pompeii now? _____

6. Scientists dig up houses, statues, and tools. _____

7. Why do they dig? _____

8. At Pompeii we can see what life was like in ancient times. _____

9. What was life like in Pompeii? _____

10. Were there beautiful paintings on the walls? _____

**The ancient city of Pompeii was destroyed by Mt. Vesuvius in A.D. 79.**

Looking Back

# Part 2

Rewrite each telling sentence as an asking sentence. Rewrite each asking sentence as a telling sentence. There is more than one correct way to write each sentence.

11. Was Pompeii by the sea?

   _____

12. Ships carried wine and oil from the harbor.

   _____

13. Volcanoes are dangerous.

   _____

14. Do you want to learn about the history of Pompeii?

   _____

# Part 3

Draw a picture of a volcano below. Next to the picture, write a question that someone might ask about the volcano. Then write your answer.

Q: _____

_____

A: _____

_____

Name _____

Looking Back

These stone ruins used to be a huge city!

Take a photo of that building.

**Circle the sentence that gives a command. Write the mark it ends with here.** _____

**Now write the mark the other sentence ends with here.** _____

Some sentences **give a command**. This kind of sentence usually ends with a period. Other sentences **express strong feelings**. This kind of sentence ends with an exclamation point.

See Handbook | Sections 6 and 9

# Part 1

Put an exclamation point at the end of each sentence that shows strong feeling. Put a period at the end of each sentence that gives a command.

1. Hey, they just found something underground ___

2. Tell everyone to come here ___

3. Wow, it's a giant statue of the Buddha ___

4. Call the director of archaeology ___

5. The statue could be 900 years old ___

6. Measure how big it is ___

7. Do not climb on the ruins ___

8. In the 12th century, Angkor was one of the world's largest cities ___

9. This city in Cambodia had more than 100 temples ___

10. I can't believe that this beautiful city was later abandoned ___

# Part 2

Pretend that you are an archaeologist. Write a command you might give one of your workers. Then write a sentence that shows a strong feeling about discovering something.

11. Gives a command: _hary give me_
_The tooth brush.._

12. Shows a strong feeling: _oh my word._
_____

# Part 3

Draw a picture of an ancient treasure scientists might dig up. If possible, use a computer graphics program to do this. Then write a sentence that shows strong feeling about what the picture shows.

_____

_____

_____

Name _____

Looking Back

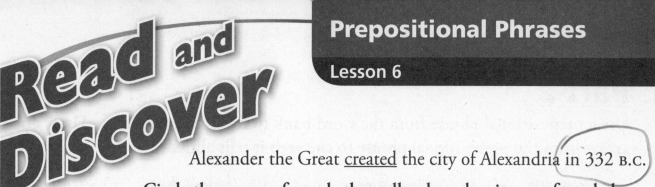

Alexander the Great <u>created</u> the city of Alexandria in 332 B.C.

**Circle the group of words that tells when the city was founded. Draw an arrow from those words to the underlined word.**

A **prepositional phrase** is a group of words that begins with a preposition. *In, with,* and *during* are prepositions. Prepositional phrases often tell more about what happened in a sentence. They usually tell *how, when,* or *where.*

**See Handbook   Section 18**

# Part 1

Draw a line under each prepositional phrase that tells about the words in bold type.

1. The ancient city of Alexandria **stood** on Egypt's shores.

2. A giant lighthouse there **soared** into the sky.

3. Its bright light **guided** boats into the harbor.

4. Visitors **gazed** at the amazing tower.

5. The lighthouse **toppled** during a huge earthquake.

6. Pieces of the monument **disappeared** into the sea.

7. Now, experts **dive** in the harbor.

8. They **photograph** stone blocks with underwater cameras.

9. Giant statues also **rest** under the sea.

10. Each ancient object **provides** another clue to scientists.

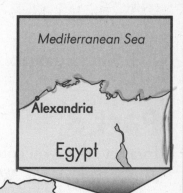

Mediterranean Sea

Alexandria

Egypt

Egypt

AFRICA

Looking Back

17

# Part 2

Use a prepositional phrase from the word bank to finish each sentence. Draw an arrow from the prepositional phrase to the verb it tells about.

| on a cliff | into pieces | below the ocean's surface |

11. Divers search _below the ocean's salface_.

12. The lighthouse stood _on a cliff_.

13. An earthquake broke that tower _into Pieces_.

# Part 3

Imagine that you could design a monument for your town or city. Draw a picture of the monument. Write two sentences about it. Use a prepositional phrase in each sentence to tell *how, when,* or *where.*

14. _____

_____

15. _____

_____

Name _____

Looking Back

Children in ancient Athens.
They played with dolls, tops, and balls.

160/A+

**Underline the group of words that is not a complete sentence.**

**Complete Sentences** have both a subject and a predicate. **Fragments** are not sentences because they do not express a complete thought. They are missing either a subject or a predicate.

See Handbook Section 12

# Part 1

Write *F* next to each fragment.

1. Athens was a great city in ancient Greece. ___

2. Large stone temples and tall statues. _F_

3. In honor of the city's favorite goddess, Athena. ___

4. People in Athens thought of many new ideas. ___

5. Especially poets, scientists, and teachers. ___

6. The idea of democracy. _F_

7. Began in ancient Athens. _F_

8. In a democracy, all citizens can vote. ___

9. Choosing their leaders. _F_

10. Not everyone in Athens was a citizen. ___

11. For instance, women and enslaved people. ___

12. None of them could vote. _F_

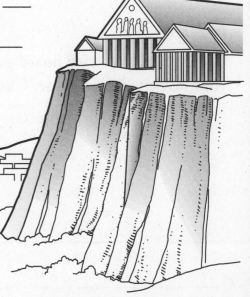

**Many great temples were built on a hill above Athens called the Acropolis.**

## Looking Back

19

# Part 2

**Underline the three fragments in the paragraph below. Rewrite them as complete sentences by adding either a subject or a predicate.**

Usually only boys went to school in ancient Athens. In our school my classmates. In ancient Greece, students played musical instruments and sang. Play musical instruments today, too. Students in Athens also studied reading, writing, and arithmetic. My favorite subject.

13. _____

_____

14. _____

_____

15. _____

_____

# Part 3

**Children played with board games in ancient Athens. Write two sentences about your favorite board game. Choose words from these lists if you like.**

| Words for Subjects | Words for Predicates |
|---|---|
| players | move |
| dice | win |
| pieces | roll |

_____

_____

_____

Name _____

Looking Back

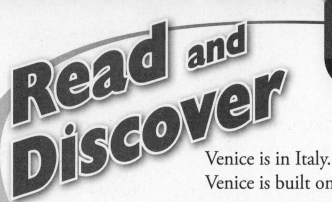

Venice is in Italy.

Venice is built on 120 small islands near the coast of Italy.

**Circle the sentence that gives more information.**

Sentences **give more information** when they include describing words or phrases and when they include words with exact meanings. For example, *gliding* is more exact than *moving*.

**Remember this information when you speak, too.**

See Handbook  Sections 14 and 17

# Part 1

Write *X* next to the sentence in each pair that gives more information.

1.  a.  Venice has been an important seaport since A.D. 800. ___

    b.  Venice is a very old city that has existed for a long time. ___

2.  a.  Venice has canals. ___

    b.  Many of the main streets in Venice are not paved streets at all, but canals filled with water. ___

3.  a.  Some people use boats. ___

    b.  Some people travel to work in boats instead of cars. ___

4.  a.  Palaces of marble and stone line Venice's Grand Canal. ___

    b.  There are a lot of fancy buildings in Venice. ___

5.  a.  Venice is famous for its beautiful buildings and collections of priceless art. ___

    b.  There is a lot to see in Venice. ___

6.  a.  Floods are a problem, and people worry about them a lot. ___

    b.  In winter, floods often cause damage to buildings in Venice. ___

7.  a.  Some Venetians build their houses on wooden posts driven into the mud. ___

    b.  Some houses in Venice are unusual. ___

## Part 2

**Rewrite each sentence so it gives more information about the picture.**

8. Visitors rode in a gondola.

   _____

   _____

9. A gondola is a boat.

   _____

   _____

10. There were some ducks.

    _____

    _____

## Part 3

**Make a travel poster that tells about your community. Describe one interesting thing to see or do there. You may use a graphics program to make another version of your poster.**

```
┌─────────────────────────────────────────────┐
│                          _____ │
│                          _____ │
│                          _____ │
│                          _____ │
└─────────────────────────────────────────────┘
```

Name _____

Looking Back

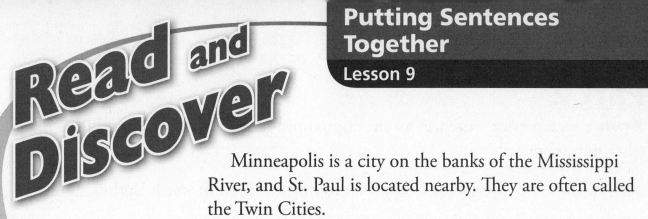

Minneapolis is a city on the banks of the Mississippi River, and St. Paul is located nearby. They are often called the Twin Cities.

**Underline the sentence that contains two complete thoughts. Circle the word that joins the two thoughts.**

A **compound sentence** contains two complete thoughts. A compound sentence is made of two simple sentences connected by a joining word such as *or, and,* or *but*. A comma is used before the joining word.

See Handbook  Sections 8, 12, and 19

# Part 1

**Underline the nine sentences below that contain two complete thoughts. Circle the joining word in each of these compound sentences. (1–9)**

Minneapolis is the largest city in Minnesota, but St. Paul is the state capital. Both cities have interesting histories.

The Sioux people first lived in this area, and their language helped give Minneapolis its name. *Minne* means "water" in the Sioux language, and *polis* means "city" in Greek. *Minneapolis* means "city on the water." The Sioux lost their claim to the land long ago, but today Minneapolis still has a large Native American population.

In the early 1800s a U.S. Army fort was built on the Mississippi River, and settlements grew up around it. In time, this center for pioneers became the city of Minneapolis. In about 1840 a trader nicknamed Pig's Eye left the fort, and he founded a little settlement farther down the river. He named the place after himself. The people in the settlement later changed the name to St. Paul, or the city might still be called Pig's Eye.

Today the two big cities are right next to each other, but they are very different. Minneapolis is an important business center, and St. Paul is known for its friendly neighborhoods.

Looking Back

# Part 2

Rewrite each pair of sentences as one compound sentence. Use the word in
( ) to join them.

10. Minnesota is very cold in winter. People must dress in warm clothes. (and)

    _____

    _____

11. Once shoppers had to walk outside in the cold. Now they can walk inside a
    gigantic mall. (but)

    _____

    _____

12. People can shop in stores. They can go to an indoor amusement park. (or)

    _____

    _____

# Part 3

Read the compound sentence below. Then write two more compound sentences.
Tell what you wear in winter and summer. You can use phrases in the word bank.

| | | |
|---|---|---|
| wear shorts | wear warm pants | wear a wool hat |
| wear boots | wear sandals | wear mittens |

Lisa wears a sweater in winter, but she wears a T-shirt in summer.

_____

_____

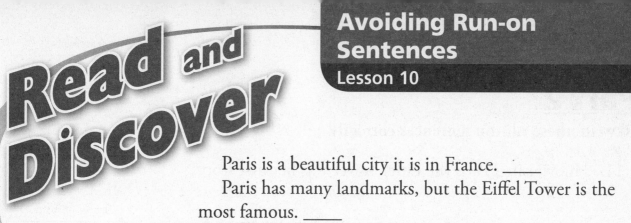

Paris is a beautiful city it is in France. _____

Paris has many landmarks, but the Eiffel Tower is the most famous. _____

**Write _X_ next to the sentence that is not written correctly. How many complete sentences can you find in it?** _____

**Run-on sentences** contain two complete sentences that are not joined by a comma and a joining word. A run-on sentence can be corrected by adding a comma and a joining word or by making the run-on into two separate sentences.

See Handbook  Section 12

# Part 1
Circle each run-on sentence.

1. The Eiffel Tower is 984 feet tall it is made of iron and steel.

2. It was designed by Alexandre Gustave Eiffel it was built in 1889.

3. Mr. Eiffel also helped build the Statue of Liberty.

4. The Eiffel Tower was once the tallest structure in the world visitors still admire its height.

5. The tower is crisscrossed it has no outer walls.

6. It was built for a fair, but the fair ended more than 100 years ago.

**The Eiffel Tower**

7. There are stairs in the tower most people prefer to take the elevator.

8. The tower has rooms for experiments, and scientists study the weather there.

9. Visitors can eat at the tower restaurants, or they can admire the view.

10. From the Eiffel Tower people can see all of Paris it is a beautiful sight.

Looking Back

# Part 2

**Rewrite these run-on sentences correctly.**

11. Huoy visited Paris the Eiffel Tower was her first stop.

    _____

    _____

12. She rode an elevator to the top her friends stayed on the ground.

    _____

    _____

13. She looked out from the tower she could see for miles.

    _____

    _____

14. Huoy gave a report about Paris she made a drawing of the Eiffel Tower.

    _____

    _____

# Part 3

**The directions below tell how to build a tower. Rewrite them correctly.**

First pour the cement then put up the iron beams next build the first floor add crisscrossed iron beams until the tower is 984 feet tall.

_____

_____

_____

Name _____

Looking Back

# Proofreading
## Practice

Read this report about Aztec art and find the mistakes. Use the proofreading marks below to show how each mistake should be fixed.

### Proofreading Marks

| Mark | Means | Example |
|------|-------|---------|
| ℯ | take away | Be careful with that that statue. |
| ∧ | add | Be careful with that statue. |
| ≡ | make into a capital letter | be careful with that statue. |
| / | make into a lowercase letter | Be Careful with that statue. |
| ⊙ | add a period | Be careful with that statue⊙ |
| sp | fix spelling | Be carefull with that statue. |

## The Aztec Display

Rodolfo and I went to see a dissplay of Aztec art. our tour guide was named Sabrina. She answered our questions about the aztec people and their art.

The collection came from Mexico City. A huge Aztec temple once stood in the center of the city it was buried long ago. In 1978 workers who were digging tunnels uncovered part of the temple. They must have been surprised.

Scientists were very excited by the discovery. They dugg carefully with shovels and other tools. The scientists found jewelry, pottery, statues, and skeletons. They learned many things about the Aztec people from those objects. The temple itself is over 550 years old scientists believe it was the center of the Aztec Empire.

The most interesting things in the display were the carvings. Were very unusual. Snakes and flowers were carved on one flat peace of stone Another carving looked like a huge shell. We also saw a tiny statue of a person carved from jade.

# Proofreading
## Checklist

You can use the list below to help you find and fix mistakes in your own writing. Write the titles of your own stories or reports in the blanks on top of the chart. Then use the questions to check your work. Make a check mark (✓) in each box after you have checked that item.

### Proofreading Checklist for Unit 1

| | Titles | | | |
|---|---|---|---|---|
| Does each sentence have a subject and a predicate? | | | | |
| Have I corrected run-on sentences? | | | | |
| Have I combined sentences correctly? | | | | |
| Have I included interesting information in each sentence? | | | | |

### Also Remember . . .

| | | | | |
|---|---|---|---|---|
| Does each sentence begin with a capital letter? | | | | |
| Does each sentence end with the right mark? | | | | |
| Have I spelled each word correctly? | | | | |
| Have I used commas correctly? | | | | |

### Your Own List

Use this space to write your own list of things to check in your writing.

| | | | | |
|---|---|---|---|---|
| | | | | |
| | | | | |
| | | | | |

Name _____

Looking Back

# Review

## Sentences

**Write S next to each complete sentence.**

1. Rome and Venice are cities in Italy. _____

2. Both cities are very old. _____

3. The center of a huge empire. _____

4. Many Romans lived in apartment buildings. _____

**Add the correct end mark to each sentence.**

5. Read this book on ancient Rome _____

6. Wow, the Roman Empire was huge _____

7. How long did that empire last _____

8. Some Roman roads and bridges are still used today _____

**Rewrite each sentence so it gives more information about this chariot race.**

9. The horses ran. _____

_____

10. A man fell. _____

_____

# Fragments and Run-ons

Rewrite each fragment to make it a complete sentence. Rewrite each run-on so it includes a comma and a joining word.

11. The canals in Venice. _____

_____

12. We drank fizzy sodas we ate tasty ice cream. _____

_____

13. Took pictures of the gondolas. _____

_____

14. Espresso is a strong Italian coffee many people like it. _____

_____

# Subjects and Predicates

Underline the subject and circle the predicate of each sentence.

15. Italian food is delicious.      18. This pizza has clams on it!

16. I like pasta with tomato sauce.    19. Many Italians love fish.

17. My grandmother makes excellent ravioli.

# Prepositional Phrases

Circle the phrase that tells *how, when,* or *where* about each underlined word.

20. We <u>went</u> to an Italian restaurant.    22. My mother <u>looked</u> at the menu.

21. I <u>sat</u> between my parents.    23. My little brother <u>banged</u> on the table.

Name _____

Looking Back

# School 🏠 Home Connection

In Unit 1 of *G.U.M.* students are learning about sentences. The activities on this page give extra practice with some of the concepts students are learning. You can help your child use the information he or she is learning in school by choosing one or more activities to complete with your child at home.

## Questions and Answers  (Sentences That Tell, Sentences That Ask)

Ask your child to think about someone your family knows and write two statements and two questions about that person. Help your child turn the statements into questions and the questions into statements.

**Example**    Is Grandma coming to dinner? becomes **Grandma is coming to dinner.**

**Aunt Sally is making the soup.** becomes **Is Aunt Sally making the soup?**

## Guess Who, Guess What?  (The Subject; The Predicate)

Think of a person you and your child both know. Write half a sentence about that person, leaving out either the subject (whom or what the sentence is about) or the predicate (what the subject is doing). Then give the sentence fragment to your child to complete. Next, he or she can write half a sentence about another person and give it to you to complete. Here are some examples:

_____ always rides his bike to work.

Uncle John _____.

## Tell Me More!  (Prepositional Phrases; Making Sentences Say More)

Look through a photo album or a magazine, and work with your child to describe what is happening in the pictures. Invite him or her to use prepositional phrases to tell *how, when,* or *where.*

**Example**    Grandma visited the Grand Canyon **in 2007**.

Some common prepositions are *in, on, to, with, during, for, under, over,* and *around.*

## Then What? (The Subject; The Predicate)

Work with your child to complete the comic strip. Help your child draw a picture in the second frame. Ask your child to write a sentence about each picture. In each sentence, your child should underline the subject and circle the predicate.

## Stop That Sentence! (Putting Sentences Together; Avoiding Run-on Sentences)

The following paragraph is one very long run-on sentence. It should have been written as several sentences. Help your child rewrite the paragraph correctly. Insert periods and other end marks. Remind your child to begin each sentence with a capital letter. Also, you and your child can combine sentences by adding a comma followed by a joining word such as *and, or,* or *but*.

My cousin Samantha's birthday is next Tuesday I wanted to buy her a gift I ran out of allowance money I didn't know what to do then I remembered my art project from school I made a birdhouse from sticks and string last week Samantha loves to watch birds she even has a bird feeder outside her window I decided that the birdhouse would be the perfect gift!

Name _____

Looking Back

# Read and Discover

In 1891, a **teacher** invented a new game.
His students **played** it indoors during winter.

**Which word in bold type names a person, place, or thing?**

_____

A **noun** is a word that names a person, place, or thing.

See Handbook Section 13

# Part 1

Circle each underlined word that is a noun.

1. James Naismith <u>stuck</u> two wooden <u>baskets</u> on railings ten feet above the floor.

2. The playing <u>court</u> <u>was</u> in between the baskets.

3. Two teams of <u>students</u> <u>played</u> the game.

4. Each <u>team</u> tried to <u>throw</u> a ball into its basket.

5. The <u>sport</u> he <u>invented</u> is called basketball.

6. A kind of <u>basketball</u> was <u>played</u> in Mexico long ago.

7. It was played on a court <u>between</u> two <u>walls</u>.

8. A stone <u>ring</u> was <u>attached</u> to each wall.

9. The <u>game</u> was played <u>with</u> a rubber ball.

10. <u>Players</u> tried to knock the ball <u>through</u> a ring.

11. They <u>could</u> not use their <u>hands</u> or <u>feet</u>.

12. The players <u>hit</u> the ball with other parts of their <u>bodies</u>.

**James Naismith invented
basketball in 1891.**

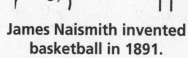

Unforgettable Folks

# Part 2

Write complete sentences to answer these questions. Circle each noun you use.

13. What is your favorite sport? _____

_____

14. What are some things that are used to play the game? _____

_____

15. Where is the game played? _____

_____

16. What do the players wear? _____

_____

# Part 3

Circle the hidden nouns. Then write them on the lines.

| B | A | S | G | D | B | F | R | O |
|---|---|---|---|---|---|---|---|---|
| A | B | H | A | T | O | R | K | P |
| S | C | E | M | U | Y | H | N | Q |
| K | P | L | E | V | A | I | J | R |
| E | X | F | B | W | W | E | K | R |
| T | E | L | E | P | H | O | N | E |
| B | F | P | Y | X | B | C | X | S |
| A | G | Q | L | Y | C | E | N | I |
| L | H | R | X | Z | D | A | K | Q |
| L | X | P | S | R | E | N | H | T |

17. _____

18. _____

19. _____

20. _____

21. _____

22. _____

23. _____

Name _____

Unforgettable Folks

In 1971 a **woman** named **Stephanie Kwolek** invented a material that was five times as strong as steel. The material was called Kevlar. The invention would make millions of dollars and save millions of lives.

**Circle the word in bold type that is the name of a certain person. Draw a box around the word that is the name of a certain thing.**

A **proper noun** names a certain person, place, or thing. Proper nouns begin with a capital letter. A **common noun** names any person, place, or thing.

See Handbook Section 13

## Part 1

Underline the proper nouns in these sentences.

1. Stephanie Kwolek was born in New Kensington, Pennsylvania.

2. She went to a college named Carnegie-Mellon.

3. Stephanie studied chemistry.

4. Then she worked at DuPont, a chemical company.

5. She created a very stiff material called Kevlar.

6. Greg, a policeman, is thankful for this invention.

7. The Kevlar in his vest saved his life last August.

8. Melinda skis, and she is also thankful.

9. The material that Ms. Kwolek invented makes skis stronger and lighter.

10. The shoes that Ramji wears are strong and flexible because of this wonderful material.

**Skis made of Kevlar are strong and light.**

## Unforgettable Folks

# Part 2

Write a proper noun of your choice to complete each sentence. Remember to start each proper noun with a capital letter.

11. I would invent a material called _The foot miss or sher blake_ .

12. A company called _yo Taylor_ would make this material.

13. I would set up this company in the state of _hallywood_ .

14. I would like to work there with my friend _Lily_ .

# Part 3

Use common and proper nouns to complete the crossword puzzle. Color each proper noun blue. Color each common noun red.

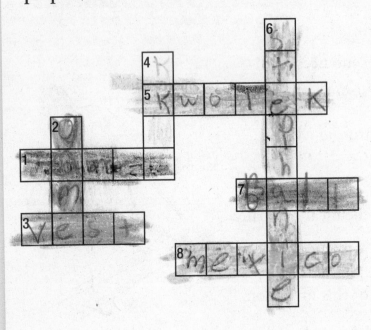

**Across**
1. Inventor of basketball (first name)
3. Protective piece of clothing made with Kevlar
5. Inventor of Kevlar (last name)
7. A toy that can be bounced
8. A country south of the United States

**Down**
2. A contest for fun
4. Equipment used to go down hills or mountains
6. Inventor of Kevlar (first name)

Name _____

Benjamin Franklin once put a metal rod on top of his **house**. Lightning hit the rod instead of the roof. The lightning traveled down a wire to the ground, and the house did not catch on fire. Soon many **houses** and other buildings had rods on their roofs.

**Which word in bold type names more than one thing?**

___houses___ Circle three other words in the paragraph that name more than one thing.

A **singular noun** names one person, place, or thing. A **plural noun** names more than one person, place, or thing. Many plural nouns are formed by adding an *s* to the end of the singular noun.

See Handbook Sections 13 and 23

# Part 1

Write *S* above the noun in bold type if it is singular. Write *P* above the noun in bold type if it is plural.

1. Ben Franklin invented a **stove** that used less fuel and made **rooms** warmer.

2. In one famous **experiment**, Franklin flew a **kite** in a thunderstorm.

3. He proved that **lightning** is **electricity**.

4. Franklin invented **lenses** that help people see **things** both near them and far away from them.

5. Franklin studied ocean **currents** and **waves**.

6. He proved that **oil** can calm rough **waters**.

7. Franklin never tried to make **money** from his **ideas**.

8. He just wanted his **inventions** to make **life** better for people.

**Bifocal lenses are one of Franklin's inventions.**

Unforgettable Folks

Kwok 37

# Part 2

Change each underlined singular noun to a plural noun. Write the plural nouns.

9. Benjamin Franklin flew the <u>kite</u>. _____

10. The <u>bolt</u> of lightning struck the kite. _____

11. Electricity traveled down the <u>string</u>. _____

12. Sparks flew from a <u>key</u> he had tied on the string. _____

13. Franklin was famous for this <u>experiment</u>. _____

# Part 3

Think of an invention that would make your life easier. Draw a picture of it in the space below. Then write about your invention. Use singular and plural nouns.

_____

_____

_____

_____

Name _____

Unforgettable Folks

# Read and Discover

Maria read a book about the famous inventor Thomas Edison. **She** learned that Edison invented the phonograph and the electric light.

**Circle a., b., or c. below to tell whom or what the word *She* talks about.**

> **a.** Edison          **b.** Maria          **c.** book

A **pronoun** takes the place of one or more nouns. Some singular pronouns are *I, you, he, she, me, him,* and *her.* Some plural pronouns are *we, you, they, us,* and *them.*

**See Handbook Section 15**

# Part 1

**Find the pronoun in each sentence. Write it on the line.**

1. Maria asked the librarian to help her find a book. _____

2. She wanted to read more about Edison. _____

3. Maria found out that he invented an early motion-picture device. _____

4. Do you know about Edison's other inventions? _____

5. I wrote a letter to the Edison Birthplace Museum in Ohio. _____

6. A woman sent me some information. _____

7. We are reading about Edison. _____

8. I read that Edison was born in 1847. _____

9. Do you want to visit Edison's workplace? _____

10. Scientists still admire the lab he built. _____

**Edison's first successful lamp looked like this one.**

## Unforgettable Folks

# Part 2

Write the pronoun from the word bank that can take the place of each underlined word or phrase.

| I | you | he | she | they |
|---|---|---|---|---|

11. <u>Thomas Edison and Benjamin Franklin</u> were two of America's greatest

inventors. _____

12. <u>Maria</u> gave a report on Thomas Edison to her class. _____

13. <u>The students</u> asked questions afterward. _____

14. <u>Steve</u> asked if Edison invented the car. _____

15. <u>Maria</u> told Steve that the car was invented by Karl Benz and

Gottlieb Daimler. _____

# Part 3

Decide which pronoun could take the place of each clue. Use those pronouns to complete the puzzle.

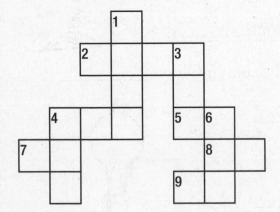

**Across**
2. Edison and Franklin
4. Thomas Edison
5. You, Steve, and me
7. You and I
8. Benjamin Franklin
9. Myself

**Down**
1. Karl Benz and Gottlieb Daimler
3. Yourself
4. Maria
6. Maria's sister

Name _____

Unforgettable Folks

# Read and Discover

In 1872, Elijah McCoy patented a cup that dripped oil onto machinery. **That** was his most famous invention. The oil cup kept machine parts from wearing out.

**What does the word in bold type refer to? Circle your answer.**

a. 1872        b. Elijah McCoy        c. the cup that dripped oil

The pronouns *this* and *these* refer to a thing or things close by. The pronouns *that* and *those* refer to a thing or things far away.

See Handbook  Section 15

## Part 1

Underline the pronoun in each sentence.

1. "This is oil," Sheila said.

2. "Put that in the car," Sheila said.

3. "The oil helps those run," Sheila continued.

4. "These may be useful, too," said Mikio.

# Part 2

Pick a pronoun from the word bank to replace each underlined phrase. Write the pronoun after the sentence.

| this | that | these | those |
|------|------|-------|-------|

5. <u>The cars over in the junkyard</u> do not run anymore. _____

6. <u>The cars next to me</u> are new. _____

7. <u>The robots beside me</u> help make car engines. _____

8. <u>The robots over there</u> put the roofs on. _____

9. <u>The tiny robot in the parking lot</u> is a clever invention. _____

10. <u>The computer I am holding</u> controls it. _____

11. <u>The switch on the wall</u> turns the lights on. _____

12. <u>The key in my pocket</u> locks the door. _____

# Part 3

Imagine that you could visit a factory that makes something you like, such as pretzels, baseballs, or games. Write about what you might see there. Use *this, that, these,* and *those.* You might want to read about that kind of factory first.

_____

_____

_____

_____

Name _____

Unforgettable Folks

In 1997 Donna Shirley's invention **rolled across** Mars.

**Which word in bold type tells what Donna Shirley's**

**invention did?** _____

An **action verb** tells what the subject of a sentence does or did.

See Handbook Section 16

# Part 1

Circle the word in bold type in each sentence that is an action verb.

1. Donna Shirley **loved** stars and **planets** as a child.

2. In high **school,** she **drew** designs for machines.

3. At age sixteen, she **flew** an **airplane**.

4. **Eventually,** Donna **moved** to California for an exciting job.

5. She **led** a **team** on a project to send a machine to explore Mars.

6. Shirley **designed** a vehicle for the **project**.

7. On July 4, 1997, a machine **traveled** on **another** planet for the first time.

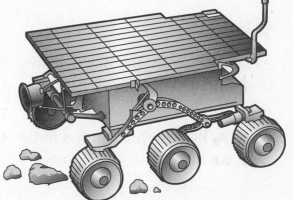

**Donna Shirley designed the Mars rover for NASA.**

8. The Mars rover **rolled** a few feet across **Mars.**

9. It **collected information**.

10. The rover **sent** amazing pictures of Mars back to **Earth**.

# Part 2

Pick three action verbs from the word bank or think of your own. Use the verbs to write three sentences that tell what the Mars rover did. Underline the action verb in each sentence you write.

| landed | traveled | photographed | rolled | gathered |

11. _____

_____

12. _____

_____

13. _____

_____

# Part 3

Answer these riddles. Each answer is a boldfaced word from page 43. Write one letter on each blank to make a word.

14. What flies but is not a bird?

__ ◯ __ ◯◯ __ ◯ __

15. What is round but cannot bounce?

◯ __ ◯◯ __

16. What is a neighbor but is millions of miles away?

◯◯ __ __

Write three action verbs that you can make from the circled letters.

_____   _____   _____

Name _____

Unforgettable Folks

Today, Ling and her friend **talk** on the telephone. Alexander Graham Bell **invented** the telephone between 1874 and 1876.

Which word in bold type shows that the action happened in the past? _____ invented _____

> **Past tense verbs** show that the action happened in the past. Many past tense verbs end in *-ed*.

Taylor

See Handbook Section 16

# Part 1

Circle the verb that fits in each sentence.

1. In 1872, Alexander Graham Bell (opens/(opened)) a school in Boston.

2. He ((trained)/trains) teachers to help deaf children.

3. Bell also (dreams/(dreamed)) of sending sounds across wires.

4. Thomas A. Watson (helps/(helped)) him find a way to do this.

5. Bell and Watson (work/(worked)) for about two years on the invention.

6. They (call/(called)) the invention the telephone.

7. Bell and Watson (show/(showed)) their telephone at a fair in Philadelphia in 1876.

**Alexander Graham Bell was fascinated with sound.**

8. One British scientist (calls/(called)) it "the most wonderful thing in America."

9. Yesterday, our class (visits/(visited)) a science museum.

10. At the museum, we (learn/(learned)) how a telephone works.

Unforgettable Folks

# Part 2

Answer these questions about you and your class. Write in complete sentences.
Use the past tense form of the underlined verbs.

11. What did you <u>learn</u> this week? _we lraned the_

   _erreya ofafe hand_

12. What games did you <u>play</u> together last week? _we play Free_

   _time_

13. What place did you <u>visit</u> together this year? _visited the_

   _zoo._

# Part 3

Find seven hidden past tense verbs. Three go across and four go down. Write
them on the lines. Circle the ending that shows they are past tense verbs.

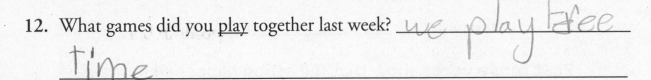

| | | | | | | | | |
|---|---|---|---|---|---|---|---|---|
| L | M | S | M | E | L | L | E | D |
| E | N | X | A | C | I | H | M | N |
| A | D | P | B | R | K | X | L | T |
| R | P | Y | L | D | E | J | O | P |
| N | R | Z | A | X | D | K | O | T |
| E | S | B | C | D | Y | L | K | A |
| D | T | S | R | E | X | E | E | L |
| H | U | S | T | A | Y | E | D | K |
| I | V | C | F | G | H | I | J | E |
| J | S | M | I | L | E | D | L | D |

14. _Liked_

15. _Smelled_

16. _Looked_

17. _Stayed_

18. _Learned_

19. _Talked_

20. _Smiled_

**Unforgettable Folks**

**Ann Moore** was **a nurse for the Peace Corps in West Africa.** She saw that mothers carried babies on their backs with cloth wraps. When she returned, Ann invented a baby carrier based on what she had seen in Africa. The carrier has helped thousands of parents.

**What word links the two groups of words in bold type?**

_____was_____

A **linking verb** does not show action. It links the subject of a sentence with other words that tell about the subject.

She **is** eight.          Saturday **was** sunny.

We **are** at school.     George and Sandy **were** funny.

See Handbook Section 16

# Part 1

Underline the linking verb in each sentence.

1. Ann Moore was a nurse for children in West Africa.

2. Cloth wraps are a traditional way of carrying babies there.

3. Ann was soon a new mother.

4. Before long, Ann's baby was a passenger on her back.

5. Carrying a baby in a twisted cloth is not easy.

6. Ann and her mother were the creators of a baby pouch.

7. It was a cozy pouch with shoulder straps.

8. This pouch was safe and easy to use.

9. The name chosen for the pouch was Snugli.

10. Many babies are passengers in Snuglis today.

**Many mothers in West Africa carry their babies in cloth wraps.**

Unforgettable Folks

## Part 2

Write a linking verb from the word bank to complete each sentence.

| is | are | was | were |
|----|-----|-----|------|

11. Many parents __were__ curious about Ann's invention.

12. The baby carrier __was__ a solution to a common problem.

13. Babies __are__ happy when they are close to a parent.

14. Earlier this morning a baby __was__ unhappy.

15. Now the baby __is__ asleep on his dad's back.

16. The mothers in West Africa __were__ an inspiration to Ann Moore.

17. Their babies __were__ calm and comfortable.

18. Baby animals in zoos __are__ sometimes carried in Snuglis.

## Part 3

Use linking verbs to join pairs of words in the word bank, and make two sentences. You can add other words to your sentences, too. Underline the linking verbs.

| Ann Moore | helpful | babies | happy |
|-----------|---------|--------|-------|

19. ann moore are helpful to parits

20. babies are happy with her invenchen

# Read and Discover

George Washington Carver was a famous <u>inventor</u>.

**Circle the word that describes the underlined word. What is another word that can tell about an inventor? Write it here.**

_____

An **adjective** describes, or tells about, a noun. Adjectives make sentences more interesting.

See Handbook Section 14

## Part 1

Circle the adjective that describes each underlined noun.

1. Dr. Carver gave farmers helpful <u>advice</u>.

2. If the farmers planted peanuts, they would soon have richer <u>soil</u>.

3. The farmers ended up with many <u>peanuts</u>.

4. The brilliant <u>inventor</u> thought of ways to use peanuts to make shampoo, ink, and margarine.

5. Dr. Carver told farmers to feed peanuts to hungry <u>cattle</u>.

6. Dr. Carver made bright <u>paints</u> out of orange peels and coffee grounds.

7. The talented <u>scientist</u> received many honors and awards.

**Dr. Carver was a scientist, a painter, an inventor, and a writer.**

## Unforgettable Folks

# Part 2

Choose an adjective from the word bank to complete each sentence.

| hard | outstanding | small | young | different | talented | new | helpful |
|------|-------------|-------|-------|-----------|----------|-----|---------|

8.  Dr. Carver was born in a _____ town in Missouri.

9.  As a _____ boy, he was interested in plants.

10. He was also a very _____ painter.

11. Young George was a _____ worker.

12. He did many _____ jobs to support himself.

13. In college he was such an _____ student that he

    became a professor right after he graduated.

14. He wrote many _____ articles about farming.

15. Farmers across the country listened to his _____ ideas.

# Part 3

Connect the dots to make a picture.

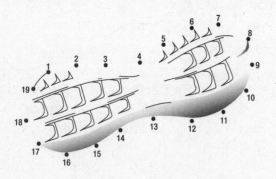

What did you draw?

_____

Write three adjectives that could describe it.

_____  _____  _____

Name _____

Unforgettable Folks

An inventor named Martine Kempf **made** and **sold** a computer device. Her device lets people speak commands to a **wheelchair** or **car**.

**What word joins the two words in bold type in the first sentence?** _____ **What word joins the two words in bold type in the second sentence?** _____

The words **and, but,** and **or** join words in sentences.

See Handbook Section 19

# Part 1

Circle the joining word in each sentence.

1. In 1948, Eleanor Raymond and Maria Telkes invented a solar house.

2. Some people did not think they could do it, but they did.

3. Outside the weather was cold, but the house was warm inside.

4. A solar house collects the sun's light and turns it into heat.

5. Power can be produced from sunlight, water, natural gas, or oil.

6. Most homes are heated by natural gas or electricity.

7. Gas heaters keep houses warm, but gas costs money.

8. Earth is running out of natural gas and oil.

9. Energy from the sun is free and doesn't pollute.

10. Kempf, Raymond, and Telkes are important inventors.

**Solar panels collect sunlight and turn it into heat.**

## Unforgettable Folks

# Part 2

Complete these sentences. Use *and,* *but,* or *or.*

11. I could be either an inventor _____

_____

12. Two of my favorite subjects are science _____

_____

13. My brother tried to invent an electric skateboard, _____

_____

# Part 3

Circle the joining word in each riddle. Then answer each riddle by writing a word in the blanks. Each answer appears somewhere on page 51.

14. I can be seen, but I can't be touched.

    What am I? _____ _____ _____

15. I can be warm, cold, rainy, or sunny.

    What am I? _____ _____ _____ _____ _____ _____ _____

16. I am wet and cool. I cover most of the earth.

    What am I? _____ _____ _____ _____ _____

Name _____

Unforgettable Folks

# Proofreading
## Practice

Read this report about kites and find the mistakes. Then use the proofreading marks below to show how each mistake should be fixed.

### Proofreading Marks

| Mark | Means | Example |
|------|-------|---------|
| ℘ | take away | The kite belongs to to Sue. |
| ∧ | add | The kite belongs to Sue. |
| ≡ | make into a capital letter | The kite belongs to sue. |
| / | make into a lowercase letter | The Kite belongs to Sue.. |
| ⊙ | add a period | The kite belongs to Sue⊙ |
| sp | fix spelling | The kite belongz to Sue. |

## Kites

People in ancient China was the first people to fly kites. Long ago, Chinese soldiers use kites to send messages. A kite's color and pattern made up a secret code. soldiers in nearby camps saw the kites. They understood the messages. Inventors in china even tried to use kite as flying machines.

In the 1800s, scientist used kites to help they understand the weather. Weather kites lifting small machines into the sky. These machines measured how cold, wet, or dry the air was. Kites were use to measure the wether until 1933.

Kites have been useful in science, too. Ben Franklin flew a kite in a storm. This experiment helped him prove that lightning is electricity. The wright brothers used a box kite to test ideas about flying. Alexander Graham Bell also experimened with box kites He thought that a group of box kites might carry a person into the air.

Today most people fly kites just for fun. Kites is fun to fly and to Watch.

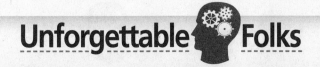

# Proofreading
## Checklist

You can use the list below to help you find and fix mistakes in your own writing. Write the titles of your own stories or reports in the blanks on top of the chart. Then use the questions to check your work. Make a check mark (✓) in each box after you have checked that item.

### Proofreading Checklist for Unit 2

| | Titles | | | |
|---|---|---|---|---|
| Have I capitalized proper nouns? | | | | |
| Have I used singular and plural nouns correctly? | | | | |
| Have I used pronouns correctly to take the place of nouns? (*I, me, we, us, you, he, she, him, her, they, them*) | | | | |
| Have I used the correct verb tenses to tell about the present and the past? | | | | |

### Also Remember . . .

| | | | | |
|---|---|---|---|---|
| Does each sentence begin with a capital letter? | | | | |
| Does each sentence end with the right mark? | | | | |
| Have I spelled each word correctly? | | | | |
| Have I used commas correctly? | | | | |

### Your Own List
Use this space to write your own list of things to check in your writing.

| | | | | |
|---|---|---|---|---|
| | | | | |
| | | | | |
| | | | | |

Name _____

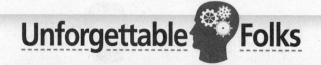
Unforgettable Folks

# Review

## Nouns

Circle the underlined words that are nouns.

1. The wheel may be the world's <u>most</u> useful <u>invention</u>.

2. The <u>wheel</u> was invented <u>about</u> 5,000 years ago.

3. The Sumerians <u>built</u> the first carts and <u>wagons</u>.

Circle the underlined words that are plural nouns.

4. The <u>invention</u> of the plow helped <u>farmers</u> grow food.

5. <u>Plows</u> are used to break up <u>soil</u>.

6. After plowing, a <u>farmer</u> can plant <u>seeds</u> easily.

Rewrite the sentences. Use a capital letter to begin proper nouns.

7. In the united states in 1837, an engineer named john deere built the first steel plow. the john deere company still makes plows today.

_____

_____

_____

## Adjectives

Circle the adjective that tells about the underlined word.

8. About 2,000 years ago, a Greek named Hero invented a helpful <u>press</u>.

9. The press could squeeze delicious <u>juice</u> from fruit.

10. Hero was a clever <u>person</u>.

# Pronouns

Write the pronoun in each sentence.

11. The ancient Sumerians gave us a great gift. _____

12. They invented the first form of writing. _____

13. That is Sumerian picture writing on the computer. _____

14. This is English writing. _____

# Verbs

Write the correct verb in ( ) to complete each sentence.

15. Long ago, people _____ heavy loads behind them. (drag/dragged)

16. The wheel _____ people move heavy loads. (helped/help)

17. Farmers _____ their crops into wagons and brought them swiftly into the cities. (load/loaded)

**Rewrite each sentence so it tells about the past.**

18. George's grandfather farms land in Indiana.

   _____

19. He uses a tractor and a plow.

   _____

# And, But, Or

Write a sentence about an inventor. Use one of these joining words: *and, but, or.*

20. _____

   _____

Name _____

Unforgettable Folks

# School 🔔🏠 Home Connection

In Unit 2 of *G.U.M.* students are learning about the jobs different words have in sentences. They are learning that **nouns**, such as *dog* and *planet,* name people, places, and things, and that **verbs** tell about actions. The activities on this page give extra practice with some of the concepts they are learning. You can help your child use the information he or she is learning in school by choosing one or more activities to complete together at home.

## Twenty Questions (Nouns)

This guessing game can be played by two to eight people. One person thinks of a person, place, or thing but keeps it a secret. The other players try to guess what noun the person is thinking of by asking questions that can be answered "yes" or "no." Guessers can ask up to twenty questions before the mystery noun is revealed.

## Dream Trip (Proper Nouns)

Work with your child to plan a dream trip he or she would like to take. The trip can be to anywhere in the world, and your child's guests can include friends, sports or movie stars, relatives, and others your child might like to invite. Help your child write a plan for the trip on a large sheet of construction paper. Include departure and return dates. Remind your child to capitalize proper nouns such as the names of cities, states, and people.

## Good Sports (Action Verbs)

Read an article from the sports section of the newspaper together. Help your child make a list of action verbs from the article. Your child might like to draw a picture for some of the more descriptive verbs you find.

## Fan Letter  (Pronouns for People)

Work with your child to write a fan letter to a person your child admires, such as a sports star, inventor, world leader, or teacher. Ask your child to make sure he or she has used pronouns (*I, me, we, us, you, he, she, him, her, they, them*) correctly. If possible, mail the letter. (You may need to help your child address the envelope.)

## Grocery List (*And, But, Or*)

The next time you make a shopping list, have your child help you. Encourage him or her to use the words *and, but,* and *or* somewhere in the list.

| Example | white **or** chocolate milk; apples **and** pears; bananas (**but** not green ones) |

## Word Search (Singular and Plural Nouns)

Circle six nouns in the puzzle.

| K | S | B | T | C | P | V | D |
|---|---|---|---|---|---|---|---|
| A | W | F | X | G | A | Z | H |
| N | P | J | Q | K | I | C | R |
| G | O | R | I | L | L | A | S |
| A | L | O | F | M | G | R | N |
| R | B | C | C | H | B | S | D |
| O | N | K | T | H | V | H | R |
| O | B | U | C | K | E | T | S |

Singular nouns name one thing. Write the singular nouns from the puzzle here.

_____

_____

_____

Plural nouns name more than one thing. Write plural nouns from the puzzle here.

_____

_____

_____

Name _____

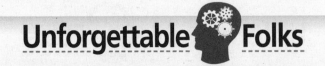
Unforgettable Folks

# Read and Discover

"**You're** playing dominoes instead of video games. I'm shocked!" said John.

"Yes! We're playing **your** favorite game," answered Brittany.

**Circle the word in bold type that means "you are."**

*Your* and *you're* sound the same, but they are spelled differently and have different meanings. *Your* means "belonging to you." *You're* is a contraction that means "you are."

See Handbook  Section 26

## Part 1

Circle the word in ( ) that belongs in each sentence.

1. "May I join (**your**/you're) game?" asked John.

2. "(Your/**You're**) welcome to play the winner," Brittany said.

3. "Okay, but (your/**you're**) playing so slowly!" grumbled John.

4. "It will be (**your**/you're) turn soon enough," said Omar.

5. "Why don't you share (**your**/you're) knowledge of the

   game with us?" Brittany suggested.

6. "Okay. The game (your/**you're**) playing

   was probably invented in China," began John.

   **The oldest set of dominoes dates back to the 12th century.**

7. "(**Your**/You're) dominoes are made out of plastic,

   but older ones were made of animal bones," he continued.

8. "(Your/**You're**) making it hard for me to concentrate," complained Omar.

Grab Bag

## Part 2

Use *your* or *you're* to complete each sentence correctly. Remember to begin every sentence with a capital letter.

9. "The game ___you're___ playing was introduced to Europeans by the Chinese in the 1300s," John explained.

10. "___Your___ dominoes have black dots, but Chinese dominoes also have red dots," he said.

11. "___You're___ really an expert on this game!" said Brittany's friend Alisha.

12. "Actually, ___your___ facts are distracting," grumbled Omar.

13. "___You're___ playing a game that is played in cafés around the world," John continued, ignoring Omar.

14. "___Your___ almost out of pieces, Brittany," remarked Alisha.

15. "I won! It's ___your___ turn to play me, John!" announced Brittany.

## Part 3

See Handbook  Section 28

Explain how to play your favorite game in an e-mail to a friend. Use *your* and *you're* correctly.

I was stacking the

Dear Lily how about

poker it will be

your turn first

Name _____

Grab Bag

"Look at those hikers **there** in the wilderness! What are they doing?" asked J.T.

"**They're** orienteering. They use maps and compasses to find **their** way," replied Darryl.

**Circle the word in bold type meaning "belonging to them." What does the word *they're* mean? Circle your answer.**
**a.** "they are"        **b.** "in that place"

The word *their*, *they're,* and *there* sound the same but have different ▮▮▮ngs and spellings. *Their* means "belonging to them." *T▮▮▮* a contraction that means "they are." *There* usually m▮▮▮ or in that place."

### See Handbook  Section 26

## Part 1

**Circle the word in ( ) th▮ ▮▮ngs in each sentence. (1–9)**

Would you enjoy trying to find your way in a wild place? Do you like to compete? If you said yes, then orienteering is for you!

Orienteers, as (they're/there) called, are experts with maps and compasses. (There/They're) usually dropped off in a wild area by off-road vehicles. The contest starts (there/they're), in the middle of nowhere. The orienteers have only (their/they're) maps and compasses to help them. They must find (their/they're) way to a certain location.

**A compass helps hikers to find their way.**

The teams all race to get (their/there) first. (Their/They're) all in a hurry. But they must take time to figure out the best way of getting to (their/they're) destination. Otherwise, (there/they're) likely to lose, or even get lost.

## Part 2

Complete each sentence with *their, they're,* or *there.* Remember to begin every sentence with a capital letter.

10. Our friends are going to the forest. Why are they going _____*There*_____?

11. _____*They're*_____ going there to learn to be orienteers.

12. Let's go over _____*there*_____ to talk to them.

13. Maybe they will let us join _____*their*_____ expedition.

14. _____*They're*_____ going to let us help read the map!

15. Here's a compass that _____*they're*_____ letting m___ ___w!

16. _____*Their*_____ compass looks very fancy.

17. I can't wait to get _____*there*_____ this weeke___

## Part 3

Write a description of a game or sport you watched people play. Use *their, they're,* and *there* at least once.

The UK game was so cool
they're going to win The carpenter
and their shots were so cool.
The wish I could go there

Name _____

Grab Bag

What game are those kids playing? **It's** called "hoop rolling," or "hoops." **Its** players run alongside rolling hoops. Each player must keep his or her hoop moving.

**Which word in bold type means "it is"? Circle it.**

*Its* and *it's* sound the same but are spelled differently and have different meanings. *Its* means "belonging to it." *It's* is a contraction that means "it is" or "it has."

See Handbook Section 26

## Part 1

Circle the word in ( ) that fits in each sentence.

1. Hoop rolling keeps (it's/**its**) players on the move.

2. (**It's**/Its) played with a very large hoop.

3. (**It's**/Its) usually made out of plastic or wood.

4. The hoop rolls well because of (it's/**its**) round shape.

5. (**It's**/Its) not likely to keep rolling by itself, though.

6. The player must help the rolling hoop keep (it's/**its**) balance.

7. (**It's**/Its) kept vertical by the player's stick.

8. The player whose hoop stays upright during (it's/**its**) whole ride is the winner.

9. While the hoop is rolling, some players try to throw a ball

   through (it's/**its**) center.

10. (**It's**/Its) hard to throw a ball through a moving hoop!

Grab Bag

# Part 2

Write *its* or *it's* to complete the sentences correctly. Remember to begin every sentence with a capital letter. (11–15)

Hoop rolling has a long history. _It's_ been played all around the world, from ancient Greece to modern America. _It's_ fun and easy to play. _It's_ equipment is not costly, so this game can be played where money is scarce. Because hoops is played in so many places, _it's_ not surprising that there are many different ways to play. In one Native American version, two players try to throw sticks through the moving hoop. Each player tries to get more sticks through _its_ center than the other does.

# Part 3

Write a description of some activity you do during recess. Use *its* and *it's* at least once.

At resses I play
kick ball It's so fun
and It's my ball,
its rules are fun

Name _____

Grab Bag

Mancala is **a** popular game in Africa. It is **an** ancient game.

**Circle the word in bold type that comes before the word beginning with a vowel sound.**

**A** and **an** are special adjectives called *articles*. Use *a* before a word that begins with a consonant sound. Use *an* before a word that begins with a vowel sound. **Remember this information when you speak, too.**

See Handbook Section 25

## Part 1

Circle the word in ( ) that fits in each sentence.

1. (A/An) mancala board has two rows of six small pits, or "buckets."

2. Each player has (a/an) extra bucket at the end of the board.

3. In (a/an) game, dried seeds might be used as playing pieces.

4. Two players start with (a/an) equal number of seeds.

5. One player scoops up all the seeds in (a/an) bucket.

6. The player drops the seeds into the buckets around the board, one seed at (a/an) time.

7. The object of (a/an) contest is to capture as many seeds as possible.

8. (A/An) group of captured seeds goes into the extra bucket.

9. The game is over when one player has (a/an) empty row of buckets.

10. When the game comes to (a/an) end, the player with more seeds in his or her bucket wins.

**Mancala may have been played first in Egypt.**

Grab Bag

# Part 2

Write *a* or *an* to complete the sentences correctly. Remember to begin every sentence with a capital letter. (11–16)

It is unusual for ___ *an* ancient game to be played all over the modern world. ____ form of mancala is popular in the Caribbean and in parts of South America today. ____ Asian version of the game is called chonka. In one African version, ____ playing board has four rows of buckets instead of two. In some places, players do not use ___ *a* board at all. They dig rows of holes in the earth! But no matter how you play it, mancala is ___ *an* exciting game!

# Part 3

Circle 5 words in the puzzle below. Each word appears in Part 1 on page 65. Then, write two sentences about the words you find. Use *a* in one sentence and *an* in the other.

| L | V | M | B | O | X | Z | K |
|---|---|---|---|---|---|---|---|
| B | Q | A | Y | I | L | T | K |
| T | U | N | B | P | H | S | J |
| J | Z | C | S | E | E | D | B |
| Y | F | A | K | K | B | C | O |
| Q | X | L | V | E | P | T | A |
| N | N | A | H | S | T | X | R |
| E | M | P | T | Y | R | D | D |

1. _____

_____

_____

2. _____

_____

_____

Name _____

66

Grab Bag

Faye is **good** at putting together puzzles, but Zoe is **better**.

Circle the word in bold type that compares two things.

The words *good* and *bad* change forms when they're used to compare. *Good* changes to **better,** and *bad* changes to **worse**. Avoid *gooder, more good, more better, badder, worser,* and *more worse*. These are always incorrect. **Remember this information when you speak, too.**

See Handbook Section 21

## Part 1

Circle the word in ( ) that fits in each sentence.

1. Zoe wants to become (better/more good) at solving number puzzles.

2. She is (more worse/worse) at them than her big sister is.

3. Emily wants a (gooder/better) shape puzzle than the one her brother gave her.

4. Faye wants to learn a (better/more better) way of identifying jigsaw puzzle

   pieces that go together.

5. Harder puzzles are (more good/better) than easier puzzles in Faye's opinion.

6. She feels (worse/worser) when she has trouble with an

   easy puzzle than when she's stumped by a hard one.

7. Zoe thinks that word puzzles are (worse/badder)

   than number puzzles.

8. Working together is a (more well/better) way of

   putting together a jigsaw puzzle than working alone.

**A jigsaw puzzle with 43,924 pieces was assembled in France in 1992.**

Grab Bag

67

# Part 2

Write four sentences comparing some activities that are fun. Tell which ones you are better at and why.

9. I am ___better___ at ___Baditball___ than ___happer___
   because ___I pactic a it is a matule___.

10. I am ___better___ at ___Kickvball___ than ___my sister___
    because ___I have a wich kick___

11. I am ___worse___ at ___walking___ than ___my DaD___
    because ___I burped my hond___.

12. I am ___worse___ at ___cloths___ than ___my mom___
    because ___she is a fashon___
    ___bisiner___

# Part 3

Write a paragraph about something you'd like to become better at. Use the words *better* and *worse* correctly.

I wood like to become
better at Just dance 3
how they Dance

Name _____

Grab Bag

Did you hear the school bell **ring**?
It **rang** late!
It has **rung** late only once before.

**Circle the word in bold type that is used with *has*.**

Some verbs do not add *-ed* to talk about the past. Their past tense forms are irregular and have **different forms**. **Remember this information when you speak, too.**

| Present | Past | With *have, has,* or *had* |
|---------|------|----------------------------|
| bring(s) | brought | brought |
| sing(s) | sang | sung |
| ring(s) | rang | rung |

See Handbook Section 16

# Part 1

Circle the word in ( ) that completes each sentence correctly. (1–11)

As soon as the school bell had (rang/rung), Jamaal ran out to the soccer field. He loved soccer so much that he (sang/sung) on his way to practice. Jamaal had (brought/brung) his own ball to school so he could start practicing without waiting for his coach.

Jamaal had a strong kick. When a ball he kicked hit the goalpost, the post (rang/ringed) like a bell. When he sent a pass skimming across the grass, the ball (singed/sang) a humming song. His pal Brian had (bringed/brought) a ball to school sometimes in the past. When he saw that Jamaal always (brang/brought) his ball, Brian no longer (brung/brought) his.

Brian and Jamaal had practiced together a lot and had (sang/sung) songs while doing drills. When Brian (sang/singed), he felt more relaxed. When the coach arrived, she (rang/rung) a bell. That was a signal for the practice to start.

Grab Bag

## Part 2

Rewrite each sentence so it tells about the past.

12. The doorbell <u>rings</u>. _The Doorbell rang_

13. Jenny <u>brings</u> me a birthday present. _Jenny brought me a birthDay gift_

14. The doorbell <u>rings</u>. (This sentence needs *has*.) _____

15. My friends <u>bring</u> birthday presents. (This sentence needs *had*.) _The Doorbell has rung my friends had_

16. They <u>sing</u> "Happy Birthday" to me. _Hough_

## Part 3

Decide which form of *bring, sing,* or *ring* fits in each clue.
Complete the puzzle.

**Across**
1. They always ___ me the phone.
2. The phone ___.
3. John had ___ the doorbell three times!

**Down**
1. He ___ me a birthday present.
4. He ___ "Happy Birthday."
5. Dolores had ___ it over the phone.

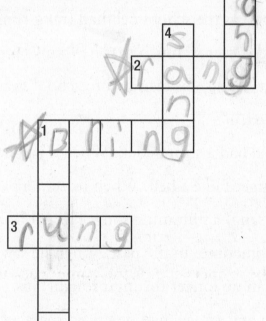

Name _____

Grab Bag

My brother and I **went** to a powwow yesterday.
We had **gone** to the same gathering last year.

**Underline the word in bold type that is used with** *had.*

Some verbs do not add *-ed* to make the past tense. They have
**different forms.** **Remember this information when**
**you speak, too.**

| Present | Past | With *have, has,* or *had* |
|---------|------|---------------------------|
| come(s) | came | come |
| go(es)  | went | gone |

See Handbook Section 16

# Part 1

Circle the word in ( ) that completes each sentence correctly.

1. We (went/gone) to a Maidu race at the powwow.

2. Someone had (came/come) early to set out rows of rocks.

3. The runners each (came/come) to the starting line, at the beginning of
   their row of rocks.

4. Suddenly the runners all (went/gone) full speed toward their farthest rock.

5. Before we could blink, they had (went/gone) past us!

6. They each grabbed their farthest rock and (came/come)
   back to the starting line.

7. The runners had (came/come) back to drop their rock at the line.

8. In a flash they (went/gone) back for the next farthest rock.

9. Our favorite runner (came/come) back first with her last rock.

10. She (went/gone) home with an award!

Grab Bag

71

## Part 2

Write a word from the word bank to complete each sentence correctly. (11–18)

| come | came | go | went | gone |
|------|------|-----|------|------|

Marvin made a kite. He had _gone_ to the store to get strips of wood and some string. Then he had _come_ home to build his kite. He used the string to make a kite shape around the wooden pieces. Next he needed a large piece of strong paper. His mom _went_ to the closet and found some heavy paper.

"Perfect!" exclaimed Marvin. He glued the paper to the string. Then he _went_ outside to let it dry.

"Mom, _come_ here! Look what I've made!" Marvin shouted. His mom _came_ outside and admired the kite. Then they _went_ to the park to try it out. "Look how high it can _go_!" Marvin yelled happily.

## Part 3

Write a short paragraph about a time you went somewhere to play a game or fly a kite. Tell who else came along. Use the past tense forms of *come* and *go*.

I went to my friends house she lived in a apartmet we played I came with a fack Bowen it was the hunger game

Name _____

Grab Bag

# Read and Discover

Making shapes with tangrams can be a **real** challenge.

~~I have a **real** good time making animal shapes.~~

**Draw a line through the sentence that uses *real* incorrectly.**

When you write, do not use *real* to mean "very." Use **real** to mean "actual or true." Use **very** to mean "to a high degree."

📣 **Remember this information when you speak, too.**

See Handbook Section 17

## Part 1

**Circle the word in ( ) that fits in each sentence.**

1. Tangrams look simple, but they can be (very/real) tricky.

2. This geometry game is (very/real) old.

3. The first (very/real) tangram puzzles were

   made long ago in China.

4. A (very/real) tangram set contains seven pieces.

5. Each tangram piece is a (very/real) simple geometric shape.

6. A player must work (very/real) quickly to put all the pieces together.

7. In a (very/real) tangram game, the pieces must make a particular shape.

8. You must be (very/real) careful to make the right shape.

9. It is a (very/real) challenge to form some shapes.

10. I find it (very/real) difficult just fitting the tangram pieces into their box!

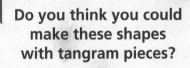

**Do you think you could make these shapes with tangram pieces?**

Grab Bag

# Part 2

Write *real* or *very* to complete each sentence correctly. (11–16)

Rubik's Cube is a game that is a ___red___

brain teaser. It's a cube with colored squares that

twist and turn. Your job is to get all the red squares

on one side, the blue squares on another side, and

so on. It sounds easy, but it is ___very___ difficult!

This game was invented accidentally by Ernö Rubik in 1974. He was

___very___ surprised to see how popular his toy became. Why has it been so

popular? It's a ___real___ challenge! Some people start playing with it and cannot

stop. They become ___very___ determined to solve the puzzle. If you give a cube

to one of these people, it can be ___very___ hard to get your cube back!

# Part 3

Find more tangram puzzles. Or, find out about another game that involves
squares, rectangles, or triangles. This could be a computer game, a game on paper,
or a game with wood or plastic pieces. Write two or more sentences about what
you learn. Use *real* and *very* in your sentences.

_____

_____

_____

_____

Name _____

**Grab Bag**

# Read and Discover

I **taken** my first lawn bowling lesson. _____ X

My grandfather **gave** me a gift. _____

**Put an X by the sentence that uses a form of *give* or *take* incorrectly.**

Some verbs do not add *-ed* to make the past tense. They have **different forms**. 📢 **Remember this information when you speak, too.**

| Present | Past | With *have, has,* or *had* |
|---------|------|----------------------------|
| give(s) | gave | given |
| take(s) | took | taken |

**See Handbook Section 16**

# Part 1

**Circle the word in ( ) that belongs in each sentence. (1–13)**

The gift was wrapped in green paper. I thanked my grandfather, and I (took/taken) the paper off. What was in the box? I (took/taken) a look inside. Wow! My grandfather had (gave/given) me four lawn bowling balls. I (gave/given) my grandfather a high five.

I have (took/taken) the balls to every lesson since then. These balls have (gave/given) me an advantage. I know how each one feels and rolls, so I play better.

How did I learn to play this game? My grandfather (took/taken) me to a match. He (gave/given) me a good sense of what the players were doing. The game began when a small white ball called the jack was rolled down the lawn. Then the players (took/taken) turns trying to roll their ball closest to the jack. Sometimes, though, a player (took/taken) a shot at the other player's ball. One player (gave/given) the other player's ball a knock that sent it to the edge of the lawn! When each player had (took/taken) four shots, the session was over. Players earned points for each ball closer to the jack than the opponent's closest ball. Several sessions were played. The first player with twenty-one points (took/taken) the prize.

Grab Bag

# Part 2

Write a word from the word bank to complete each sentence correctly.

| give | (gave) | given | take | (took) | taken |
|------|--------|-------|------|--------|-------|

14. People have _____took_____ lawn bowling seriously for a long time.

15. Historians say the ancient Egyptians _____gave_____ this game to the world.

16. Lawn bowling has _____taken_____ many different forms. France, Denmark, Italy, and Polynesia have their own ways to play.

17. Long ago, people from England and Scotland _____took_____ this game with them when they left home for America.

18. Lawn bowling was so popular then that settlers _____gave_____ many new towns the name *Bowling Green*.

19. Lawn bowling has _____taken_____ a different form in Canada. It has become the sport of curling, which is played on ice.

# Part 3

Decide which form of *give* or *take* belongs in each sentence. Write the words in the crossword puzzle.

**Across**
1. I __ a picture of my grandfather yesterday.
2. He had __ me a camera.
3. I posted the photo on a photo site. I __ him the Web address.

**Down**
1. My sister has __ pictures since she was five.
2. Grandpa had __ her a camera.
4. She __ a picture of her shoes.

Name _____

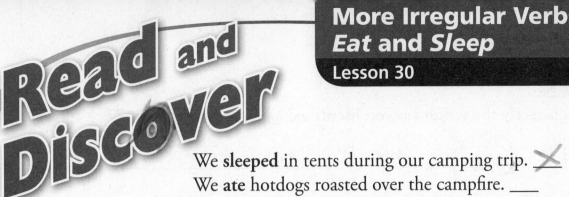

We **sleeped** in tents during our camping trip. ✗
We **ate** hotdogs roasted over the campfire. ___

Put an X by the sentence that uses a form of *eat* or *sleep* incorrectly.

Some verbs do not add *-ed* to make the past tense. They have **different forms**. Remember this information when you speak, too.

| Present | Past | With *have, has,* or *had* |
|---------|------|---------------------------|
| eat(s) | ate | eaten |
| sleep(s) | slept | slept |

See Handbook Section 16

# Part 1

Look at the verb in **bold** type in each sentence. Write *X* after the sentence if it is incorrect.

1. It was warm during the day, but it got cold outside while we **sleep**. ✗

2. We **sleeped** in sleeping bags to stay warm. ✗

3. I have **slept** under the stars many times. ___

4. Sometimes I think I **sleep** better outside than I do inside! ___

5. I like to **eaten** dinner outside, too. ✗

6. We **ate** and told stories around the campfire every night of our trip. ___

7. I have **ate** very good meals while camping. ✗

8. During one camping trip, we **eat** fish that we caught from the river! ✗

9. It was the best fish I have **eaten** in my life! ___

Grab Bag

# Part 2

Rewrite correctly the sentences you identified as incorrect on page 77.

10.  It was warm buning Day

11.  _____

12.  _____

13.  _____

14.  _____

# Part 3

Circle the word that belongs in each sentence. Then add more words to complete the sentences.

Past

15.  Yesterday I (slept/sleep) slept like I was in a match

16.  Yesterday I (ate/eat) ate T-bowen stake

Present

17.  Every day I (ate/eat) eat maspattos

18.  Every day I (slept/sleep) slept like a log

With *have, has,* or *had*

19.  I have (ate/eaten) eaten cray fish jauttos.

20.  I have (sleep/slept) I slept on my four

Name _____

78

# Proofreading
## Practice

This report is about what games children played during Colonial times. Read the report and find the mistakes. Then use the proofreading marks below to mark how the mistakes should be corrected.

### Proofreading Marks

| Mark | Means | Example |
|------|-------|---------|
| ℒ | take away | This game is ~~too~~ too easy. |
| ∧ | add | This game ^is^ too easy. |
| ≡ | make into a capital letter | t̲h̲is game is too easy. |
| / | make into a lowercase letter | This game I̸s too easy. |
| ⊙ | add a period | This game is too easy⊙ |
| (sp) | fix spelling | This game is to easy. |

## Games During Colonial Times

What kinds of games did childern play during Colonial times? They're games were simalur to the ones you and me play today. They enjoyed games of tag and blind man's bluff, an version of tag where the person who is "it" is blindfolded. They gone outside to pitch horseshoes and shoot marbles. Spinning tops was real popular. Friend would compete to see whose top could spin longest. Childern would also fly kites and roll hoops.

Another very popalar game was lawn bowling. Every Village had it's own bowling green. The game was made more dificult by using egg-shaped balls rather than perfectly round ones.

Children in Colonial times also play a game called jackstraws, which colonists learned from the American Indians To play the game, you needed straws or twigs. Each child taken a turn picking up a straw without moving the others in the pile. the winner of the game was the child who picked up the most Straws.

Grab Bag

# Proofreading
## Checklist

You can use the list below to help you find and fix mistakes in your own writing. Write the titles of your own stories or reports in the blanks on top of the chart. Then use the questions to check your work. Make a check mark (✓) in each box after you have checked that item.

### Proofreading Checklist for Unit 3

| | Titles | | | |
|---|---|---|---|---|
| Have I used *your* and *you're* correctly? | | | | |
| Have I used *its* and *it's* correctly? | | | | |
| Have I used the correct forms of *come, go, give,* and *take*? | | | | |
| Have I used *their, there,* and *they're* correctly? | | | | |

### Also Remember . . .

| | | | | |
|---|---|---|---|---|
| Does each sentence begin with a capital letter? | | | | |
| Does each sentence end with the right mark? | | | | |
| Have I spelled each word correctly? | | | | |
| Have I used commas correctly? | | | | |

### Your Own List
Use this space to write your own list of things to check in your writing.

| | | | | |
|---|---|---|---|---|
| | | | | |
| | | | | |
| | | | | |

**Name** _____

Grab Bag

Taylor
68%
NI

# Usage

**Circle the word in ( ) that completes each sentence correctly.**

1. We had (took/taken) out pictures of great soccer teams.

2. "(Their/They're) uniforms are so cool," said Crystal.

3. "Are (your/you're) uniforms blue or red?" she asked Chris.

4. "(They're/Their) blue, and our numbers are yellow," he responded.

5. "Jeremy (gave/given) us a choice of red or blue, and we chose blue."

6. "He (gone/went) to pick them up today," Chris continued.

**Circle the mistake in each sentence. Write the correct word on the lines.**

7. Chris brung the new uniforms for everyone to see. _____bring_____

8. An new uniform was passed around the room. _____uniforms_____

9. Everyone was real happy with them. _____very_____

10. Then Crystal's cell phone ringed. _____rang_____

11. "Is that you're cell phone?" asked Chris. _____your_____

12. "Its too loud!" complained Jeremy. _____It's_____

13. "Sorry guys! Sometimes it's gooder to leave the cell phone at home!"

Crystal said. _____better_____

Grab Bag

# More Usage

Taylor

Circle the word in ( ) that belongs in each sentence. Write that word on the line.

14. Shelby liked to play __an__ old string game that her grandma taught her. (a/an)

15. The players hold the string in different shapes, and __their__ fingers create complicated tangles. (they're/their)

16. In the Arctic, Inuit girls learn to make __their__ people's traditional string figures. (their/there)

17. These girls make string figures to trap the sun so it will stay __there__ longer. (their/there)

18. But Shelby had a __very__ difficult time playing the game all by herself! (real/very)

19. She __went__ outside to play marbles with her brother. (went/gone)

20. Her marble __rung__ loudly when it hit her brother's marble. (rung/rang)

21. Her brother __took__ a shot that sent a marble all the way to the end of the block! (took/take)

22. After they had __ate__ dinner, Shelby and her brother went back to the marbles game. (ate/eaten)

23. Shelby's dreams that night were all about __their__ games. (their/there)

24. Her brother already had __gone__ outside when Shelby awoke the next morning. (went/gone)

25. Shelby had __slept__ very late! (slept/sleeped)

Name _____

Grab Bag

# School 🏫 Home Connection

In Unit 3 of *G.U.M.* students are learning how to use words that can be confusing, such as *its* and *it's*. The activities on these pages give extra practice with some of the concepts students are learning. You can help your child understand the information he or she is learning in school by choosing one or more activities to complete with your child at home.

## A Musical Review (*Their, They're, There*)

Watch a musical performance with your child, either on broadcast TV or on DVD. Afterward, work together to write a review of the performance. Write about what you liked and didn't like about the performers, the music, the stage decorations, and so on. Use these words in your review: *there, their* (meaning "belonging to"), and *they're* (*they are*). Have your child make sure each of these words is used correctly.

## Wash with Care (*Its* and *It's*)

With your child, read the washing instructions on a favorite item of clothing. Help your child rewrite the label, using the words *it's* (*it is*) and *its* (meaning "belonging to"). Encourage your child to explain when each of these words should be used.

## Car for Sale (*Very* and *Real*)

Invite your child to look through the newspaper with you. Find the section of the want ads where cars are listed for sale. Read the ads together and ask your child to pick out a car he or she thinks would be fun to have. Then help your child write sentences about the car, using the words *very* and *real*.

Grab 🁫 Bag

## Board Game (*Their, They're, There; Its* and *It's*)

Ask your child to write these words on slips of paper: *their, they're,* and *there; its* and *it's.* Work together to draw a simple game board on a piece of paper. Include squares marked "Start," "Lose a Turn," "Jump Ahead One Square," and "Finish." Find a game piece for each player (an eraser, a piece of dry macaroni, or any other small object). Place the word slips in a bag. Players take turns pulling a slip from the bag and using the word correctly in a sentence. Each player moves ahead one space for each correct answer.

## You're Invited! (*Your* and *You're*)

The next time your child invites a friend to your house, help him or her write an invitation. Ask your child to use the words *you're* (*you are*) and *your* (meaning "belonging to") in the invitation.

> **Example**    **You're** going to sleep in a sleeping bag. You can keep **your** clothes in my closet. Please bring **your** skates. **You're** going to have a great time!

## Crossword Puzzle (More Irregular Verbs: *Come* and *Go*)

Work with your child to complete this crossword puzzle. Each missing word is a form of *come* or *go.*

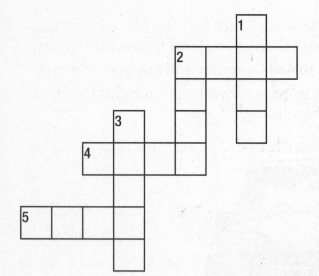

**Across**
  2. Every Saturday, John ___ to a car lot.
  4. Some of the cars have ___ from other countries.
  5. This car ___ from Germany about forty years ago.

**Down**
  1. John just ___ to the bank.
  2. He has ___ there many times before.
  3. "He always ___ here every Saturday at ten-thirty," laughed the bank teller.

Name _____

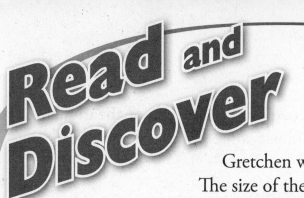

Gretchen watched a video about humpback whales. The size of the whales amazed **her**. **She** learned that whales are mammals, not fish.

One pronoun in bold type takes the place of *Gretchen* and is the subject of a sentence. Circle that pronoun.

A **subject pronoun** takes the place of one or more nouns in the subject of a sentence. *I, you, he, she,* and *it* are singular subject pronouns. *We, you,* and *they* are plural subject pronouns.

See Handbook Section 15

# Part 1

Underline eight subject pronouns in the paragraphs below. (1–8)

Humpback whales swim in groups called pods. They travel many miles every year. Many humpback whales spend the summer in the icy waters near the North Pole. They swim south again when the weather turns cold.

In the spring, a mother whale gives birth to a calf. She feeds milk to her baby. He stays by his mother's side for many months. It is a safe place for him.

In late spring, the calf follows his mother north to the waters near Alaska. He stays near his mother for a full year.

You might see some humpback whales on a summer trip to Alaska. I saw seven whales on a trip to Sitka in July.

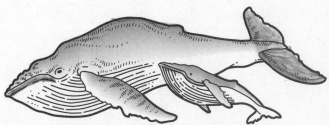

**A young whale is called a calf.**

Beasts & Critters

85

# Part 2

Write the pronoun from the word bank that could take the place of the under-lined word or words in each sentence. You can use some pronouns more than once.

| It | I | We | They | She | You | He |
|---|---|---|---|---|---|---|

9. Mrs. Sanchez took our class to the natural history museum. __she__

10. My classmates and I saw models of sea animals. __we__

11. A guide named Carlos showed us a model of a whale. __He__

12. Carlos pointed to a hole at the top of the whale's head. __He__

13. That blowhole allows the whale to breathe. __it__

14. Whales must come to the surface for air. __they__

15. Some whales can hold their breath for two hours. __they__

# Part 3

Write a subject pronoun to answer each riddle.

16. I'm found in the words *she* and *they*. Who am I? __h e__

17. I'm found in the word *it*. Who am I? __I__

18. I rhyme with *blue*. I can talk about one person or many. Who am I?

    __y__ __o__ __u__

Name _____

Beasts & Critters

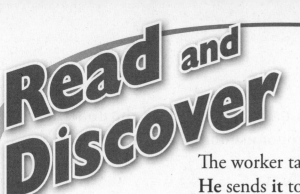

The worker takes the **egg** out of the eagle's nest.
**He** sends **it** to a research center in Oklahoma.

**In the first sentence, *egg* tells what the worker takes. Write the pronoun in the second sentence that stands for what the worker sends.** _____it_____

An **object pronoun** takes the place of one or more nouns. Object pronouns come after action verbs and words such as *to, at, for, of,* and *with.* Singular object pronouns are *me, you, him, her,* and *it.* Plural object pronouns are *us, you,* and *them.*

**See Handbook Section 15**

# Part 1

**Underline ten object pronouns in the sentences below. (1–10)**

A jet carries several eggs to the research center. There a woman unpacks them carefully. She puts them into a warm incubator.

Later a tapping noise excites her. The woman calls to a helper. She tells him the sound is a chick pecking at its shell. They look at the egg and see big cracks in it.

After the tiny eagle has hatched, the woman puts it between a pad and a towel. The chick rubs against them to dry off. After a while the woman calls to the helper.

"Please bring the puppet to me."

He brings it to her. The puppet looks like a mother eagle's head. The woman uses the puppet's beak to pick up some meat.

The little chick opens its mouth and grabs the meat. Yum yum! The chick is ready for more!

**This chick takes food from a puppet that looks like a mother eagle.**

# Part 2

Write a pronoun from the word bank that could take the place of the underlined words in each sentence. You will use some pronouns more than once.

| I | me | it | him | we | us |
|---|---|---|---|---|---|
| you | he | she | her | they | them |

11. The workers care for <u>the eagles</u> for eight weeks. _Them_

12. Small birds, fish, and meat are served to <u>the hungry eagles</u>. _Them_

13. The man helps <u>the woman</u> with the feeding. _her_

14. She asks <u>the man</u> to take the young eagles to a private area. _him_

15. Eagles must hunt <u>birds and animals</u> for food. _Them_

16. Tomorrow the woman will bring the eagle with <u>the woman</u> and set it free.

    _her_

17. Maybe the eagle will fly over <u>you and me</u> someday. _us_

18. Do you see <u>the eagle's nest</u> in that tree? _it_

# Part 3

Find seven pronouns that can be used as object pronouns. Circle them.

| H | I | M | L | N | R |
|---|---|---|---|---|---|
| C | T | K | Y | O | U |
| M | B | W | P | H | D |
| E | G | T | H | E | M |
| J | U | S | Q | R | V |

Name _____

Beasts & Critters

# Read and Discover

I went to the zoo.
An elephant sprayed water at I.

Circle the sentence in which *I* is the subject. Cross out the sentence in which *I* is used incorrectly as an object.

Use *I, we, he, she,* and *they* as **subjects** of sentences. Use *me, us, him, her,* and *them* as **objects** in sentences.

See Handbook Section 15

# Part 1

Underline the correct word in ( ) to complete each sentence.

1. (I/Me) met my sister at the front gate.

2. (She/Her) wants a job as a zookeeper.

3. My sister told (I/me) interesting facts about elephants.

4. I asked (she/her) why elephants spray water on themselves.

5. (She/Her) told me that the water helps them keep cool.

6. An adult elephant's trunk is strong enough to lift (we/us) together!

7. (We/Us) saw two elephants greet each other.

8. (Them/They) put their trunks in each other's mouths!

9. A trunk is as important to an elephant as hands are to (I/me).

**Elephants love water, and they are very good swimmers.**

# Part 2
Write the pronoun that you could use to stand for the word or words in ( ).

10. _____ played a computer game about animals in danger. (Fran and I)

11. ___She___ tried to stop hunters from killing elephants. (Fran)

12. ___They___ wanted the ivory in the elephants' tusks. (the hunters)

13. I helped ___her___ with the game. (Fran)

14. We did not arrest ___them___. (the hunters)

15. We sent ___him___ to teach the hunters how to grow valuable crops. (a man)

# Part 3
Write the pronoun that completes each poem. Use each pronoun only once.

| us | me | I |
|---|---|---|

16. There's an elephant on the bus.

    Will there be any room for ___us___?

17. We passed an elephant in a tree.

    I hope it doesn't fall on ___me___.

18. Then my brother and ___I___

    Saw something huge in the sky.

    We didn't know elephants could fly!

Name _____

**Beasts & Critters**

I wrote a report on buffalo. Luis gave **me** a book about them.

What if Sally worked with the speaker to write the report? What if Sally was given the book, too? Rewrite both sentences. Add the words *Sally and* to each sentence.

*Sally and I wrote a report on theB*
*Luis gave me a book about them.oo*
*K*

*I* is a **subject pronoun**. It can be used as the subject of a sentence. *Me* is an **object pronoun**. It is used after an action verb or words such as *to, at, for, of,* or *with*. When you talk about yourself and another person, always name the other person first.

📣 **Remember this information when you speak, too.**

See Handbook Sections 15 and 25

# Part 1

Write *I* or *me* to complete each sentence correctly.

1. Carla and ___I___ visited a park in Montana last fall.

2. A buffalo calf walked toward Carla and _me_ .

3. Carla and ___I___ took pictures of the calf.

4. At the museum, a park ranger talked to Carla and _me_ .

**The National Bison Range is in Montana.**

5. She told Carla and _me_ that the proper name for American buffalo is *bison*.

6. Carla and ___I___ learned that some Native Americans hunted bison.

7. Carla and ___I___ saw tools and a tepee made from bison bones and hides.

8. The ranger showed Carla and _me_ a map of where bison once lived.

## Beasts & Critters

# Part 2

Write the correct words in ( ) to complete each sentence.

9. ___*Luis and I*___ walked on part of the old Bozeman Trail.
(Me and Luis/Luis and I)

10. A woman showed ___*me and luis*___ some bison bones.
(Luis and me/me and Luis)

11. ___*luis and I*___ learned that millions of bison roamed the plains in
pioneer days. (Luis and I/I and Luis)

12. The woman walked with ___*Luis and me*___ to some railroad tracks.
(Luis and me/Luis and I)

13. She told ___*Luis and me*___ that people shot bison from the train
windows. (me and Luis/Luis and me)

14. ___*Luis and I*___ are both glad that the bison were not all killed.
(Luis and I/Me and Luis)

15. _____ hope that there will always be buffalo in
Montana. (I and Luis/Luis and I)

# Part 3

Complete this poem by making it tell about you and a friend of yours. Use *I* or
*me* to refer to yourself.

___*Lily*___ and ___*I*___ wanted to know,

Where did all the bison go?

A ranger told ___*Lily*___ and ___*me*___,

"There are still a few to see."

Name _____

Beasts & Critters

a. Wanda **she** visited a giant panda in the zoo.
b. **She** watched the panda eat bamboo shoots.

**Which sentence makes sense if you take out the word *she*?**

_____

A **subject pronoun** takes the place of one or more nouns in the subject of a sentence. Do not use the subject pronoun right after the noun it stands for. **Remember this information when you speak, too.**

See Handbook Section 15

# Part 1

The subject pronouns are underlined below. Draw a line through a subject pronoun if it is **not** needed in the sentence. (1–10)

Giant pandas are native to China. A mother panda ~~she~~ gives birth once a year. <u>She</u> bears one or two tiny cubs. Each cub ~~it~~ weighs about five ounces. The cubs ~~they~~ are helpless. <u>They</u> must stay with their mother all the time.

Bamboo plants are the giant pandas' favorite food. Pandas ~~they~~ eat up to 85 pounds of bamboo each day. Pandas will eat meat, but <u>they</u> have a difficult time getting any. <u>They</u> are not good hunters.

The bamboo plants can cause big problems for giant pandas. About every 100 years, all the bamboo plants grow seeds and then die. The bamboo seeds ~~they~~ may take a few years to grow into plants. The pandas do not have enough to eat until the new plants grow. Some of the pandas ~~they~~ starve to death.

**An adult giant panda weighs between 200 and 300 pounds.**

# Part 2

Cross out the extra pronoun in each sentence. Then rewrite the sentence correctly.

11. Giant pandas ~~they~~ are an endangered species. _Giant pandas are an endangered species_

12. Zhen-Zhen ~~she~~ was a giant panda. _Zhen-Zhen was a giant panda_

13. The name Zhen-Zhen ~~it~~ means "precious" in Chinese. _The name Zhen-Z means "precious" in chinese_

14. This panda ~~she~~ lived in a nature reserve in China. _This panda lived in a nature reserve in_

15. Scientists ~~they~~ studied her to learn how to help pandas survive. _____

_____

# Part 3

**See Handbook  Section 30**

The panda is a plant eater, eating up to 85 pounds of bamboo each day. Have an adult help you search the Internet to learn about other large animals that are plant eaters. Write three facts you learn. Use pronouns correctly.

_____

_____

_____

Name _____

Beasts & Critters

Baby **gorillas** <u>make</u> different kinds of noises.
A scared baby **gorilla** <u>makes</u> a soft crying noise.

Circle the word in bold type that tells about one thing.
Does the verb that follows that word end in *s*? _yes_
Draw a box around the word in bold type that tells about more than one thing.
Does the verb that follows that word end in *s*? _no_

The **subject** and its **verb** must **agree**. Add *s* or *es* to a regular verb in the present tense when the subject is a singular noun or *he, she,* or *it*. Do not add *s* or *es* to a regular verb in the present tense when the subject is *I, you, we,* or *they*. 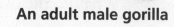 **Remember this information when you speak, too.**

See Handbook Section 16

# Part 1

Underline the subject of each sentence. Decide whether it names one thing or more than one thing. Circle the verb in ( ) that fits in each sentence.

1. Gorillas (live/lives) in groups in the rainforests of Africa.

2. An adult male gorilla (live/lives) with female gorillas and their young.

3. The male (protect/protects) the group.

4. The group members (find/finds) a new place to sleep each night.

5. Each adult (build/builds) a sleeping nest.

6. A baby (sleep/sleeps) in its mother's nest.

7. Baby gorillas (walk/walks) at the age of five months.

8. A female (care/cares) for her baby for three years.

9. These large mammals (eat/eats) fruit, leaves, and bark.

10. A gorilla (show/shows) affection by combing its fingers through another's fur.

**An adult male gorilla**

# Part 2

**Rewrite the sentences using the correct verb form in ( ).**

11. The two-year-old gorilla (play/plays) with her younger sister. _The_
_Two year old gorilla plays with her younger sister_

12. They (tumble/tumbles) across the forest floor. _They tumble_
_across the forest flr_

13. The little sister (run/runs) away. _The little sister away_

14. She (go/goes) to the river for a drink of water. _____

# Part 3

**Unscramble each verb in ( ) and write it on the lines. Be sure the verb agrees with the subject. Unscramble the circled letters to answer the question.**

15. Two young gorillas _p l a y_ in the forest. (yalp)

16. One of them _c l i m b s_ a tree. (lcibms)

17. The other one _h u n t s_ for something to eat. (shunt)

18. She _f i n d s_ a yellow treat. (difns)

19. Together they _s h a r s_ the snack. (hares)

20. It _____ sweet. (atesst)

    What do the two gorillas eat? A _bannas_

Name _____

That big **wolf** is a timber wolf.
Those **wolves** are endangered.

The word in bold type that tells about one animal is a singular subject. What verb is used with it? _____
The word in bold type that tells about more than one animal is a plural subject. What verb is used with it? _____

Use *is* or *was* after a **singular subject**. Use *are* or *were* after a **plural subject**. 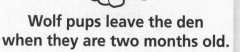 Remember this information when you speak, too.

See Handbook Sections 16 and 25

# Part 1

Write *S* after each sentence with a singular subject. Write *P* after each sentence with a plural subject. Circle the word in ( ) that fits in each sentence.

1. The wolf (was/were) alone until he found a mate. _P_

2. She (are/is) in the den. _S_

3. The newborn wolf pups (are/is) with her. _P_ hi

4. These pups (is/are) too young to hunt. _P_

5. They (was/were) asleep moments ago. _P_

6. Now they (is/are) hungry for their
   mother's milk. _P_

7. The smallest pup (is/are) adventurous and leaves the den. _S_

8. His brothers and sisters (are/is) not ready to join him. _P_

9. Yesterday the pup and a sister (was/were) outside for an hour. _P_

**Wolf pups leave the den
when they are two months old.**

# Part 2

Choose the word in ( ) that fits in each sentence. Write the word on the line.

10. The hungry wolves _____were_____ ready to hunt. (was/were)

11. Healthy elks _____are_____ faster than the wolves. (is/are)

12. One elk _____was_____ sick and could not escape. (was/were)

13. The hunt _____were_____ over quickly. (was/were)

14. The loss _____ars_____ helpful to the elk herd. (is/are)

15. Now the other elks _____are_____ less likely to get sick. (is/are)

# Part 3

Find all three wolves in the picture. Rewrite the sentence to tell about the picture.

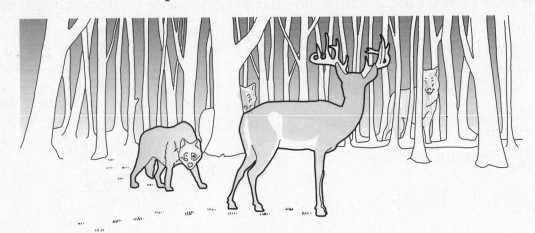

One wolf is watching the deer.

Three Wolves were

waching Dera

Name _____

Beasts & Critters

a. Long ago, some sailors **believed** that manatees were mermaids.

b. These large, blubbery marine animals **live** in warm waters.

**Which sentence tells about something that happened in the past? _____ Circle the last two letters in the boldfaced verb in that sentence.**

The **tense** of a verb helps show when an action happens. A past tense verb shows that the action happened in the past. Many past tense verbs end in -*ed*.

See Handbook Section 16

# Part 1

**The verbs in the paragraphs below are in bold type. Circle each past tense verb. (1–10)**

Long ago, many manatees **lived** in the waters around Florida. They **grazed** on underwater plants. Each day, they **ate** a pound of food for every 10 pounds of their body weight.

In the 1990s, many manatees **died**. Boaters **zoomed** through the manatees' habitat at high speeds. Their boats **collided** with the slow-moving manatees. Pollution **caused** the deaths of other manatees.

Today the manatees still **swim** slowly in shallow water. But laws **restrict** boaters from going too fast. Boats **hit** them less frequently now.

A manatee's upper lip is split into two strong muscles that allow it to grab and eat aquatic plants.

## Part 2

Rewrite each sentence. Change the underlined verb so it tells about an event that happened in the past.

11. Joan <u>paddles</u> up to the manatee in the lagoon. *Joan paddled*

_____

12. She <u>watches</u> the fearless manatee. *She watches*

13. It <u>moves</u> slowly through the water like an underwater blimp. _____

_____

14. In shallow water, the manatee <u>walks</u> using its flippers. _____

_____

15. The manatee <u>surfaces</u> for air every three or four minutes. _____

_____

## Part 3

Circle the past tense form of each of these verbs in the puzzle: *bow, jump, greet, perform, walk, watch.*

| D | W | A | T | C | H | E | D | N |
|---|---|---|---|---|---|---|---|---|
| E | A | S | P | B | N | L | A | R |
| R | L | O | Q | E | I | J | S | J |
| I | K | A | U | B | C | U | G | O |
| P | E | R | F | O | R | M | E | D |
| F | D | I | R | W | O | P | D | F |
| S | G | R | E | E | T | E | D | G |
| A | N | E | D | D | Q | D | K | H |

Name _____

Beasts & Critters

Most bats are **not** dangerous to people. Do **not never** touch a wild bat, though. It might have rabies.

Each word in bold type means "no." Underline the sentence that has just one word that means "no."

A **negative** is a word that means "no" or "not at all." *No, not, nothing, none, never, nowhere,* and *nobody* are negatives. Words that have *not* in them, like *can't* and *don't,* are negatives, too. Do not use two negatives in the same sentence. **Remember this information when you speak, too.**

See Handbook **Section 20**

# Part 1

Underline each negative in the sentences below. Write *X* after each sentence that has too many negatives.

1. Bats are not blind. _____

2. Bats do not have good eyesight, though. _____

3. Most female bats don't have no more than one baby a year. _____

4. Some bats cannot find nothing to eat during the winter, so they sleep. _____

5. No mammal besides the bat can truly fly. _____

6. Bats come out at night but are usually nowhere to be seen in the daytime. _____

7. Most vampire bats never bite no people. _____

8. Bats do not turn people into no vampires. _____

9. Most people don't know how helpful bats are. _____

10. No other creature doesn't eat as many insects at night as a bat does. _____

**Bats spend daylight hours in dark, sheltered places.**

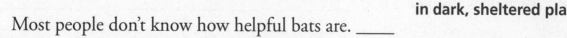

# Part 2

Rewrite each sentence so it has just one negative. There is more than one correct way to rewrite each sentence.

11. Most bats do not never hunt during the day. _____

_____

12. Bats don't never build nests. _____

13. Bats that eat fruit don't need nothing much to drink. _____

_____

14. Lea didn't see no bats until twilight. _____

_____

15. Martin did not know nothing about bats until he visited Carlsbad Caverns

National Park. _____

_____

# Part 3

Read the sentence pair below. Then write a sentence to give one reason why a dog, a snake, and a whale are not like a bat. Use negatives in your sentences.

A cow is not like a bat. A cow never hangs upside down!

16. A dog is not like a bat. _____!

17. A snake is not like a bat. _____!

18. A whale is not like a bat. _____!

Name _____

Beasts & Critters

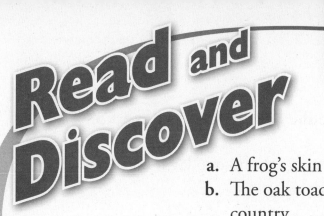
**Read and Discover**

a. A frog's skin is **smoother** than a toad's skin.
b. The oak toad is the **smallest** toad in this part of the country.

Which sentence compares two things? _____ What letters were added to the adjective *smooth* in this sentence? _____
Which sentence compares one thing to all other things of that kind? _____ Which letters were added to *small* in that sentence? _____

An **adjective** can describe by **comparing** two persons, places, or things. Add *-er* to short adjectives to compare two things. (For example, use *smoother* instead of *more smooth*.) An adjective can also compare more than two persons, places, or things. Add *-est* to short adjectives to compare more than two things. (For example, use *smallest* instead of *most small*.) **Remember this information when you speak, too.**

**See Handbook** Section 21

# Part 1

Underline the word or words in ( ) to complete each sentence correctly.

1. A male frog has a (louder/more loud) voice than a female frog.

2. Bullfrogs have the (deepest/most deep) voices of all frogs.

3. The goliath frog is the (largest/more large) of all frogs.

4. A frog's skin is (wetter/more wet) than a toad's skin.

5. Toads have (more short/shorter) back legs than frogs.

6. Toads have (wider/more wide) bodies than frogs.

7. Some toads live in the (hottest/most hot) deserts.

8. These animals would be (safer/more safe) if humans didn't destroy their homes.

**This toad is catching an insect with its tongue.**

**Beasts & Critters**

# Part 2

Add *-er* or *-est* to the adjective in ( ). Write the new word on the line.

9. The students are taking a _____ hike today than the one they took yesterday. (long)

10. The sky is _____ now than it was a few minutes ago. (dark)

11. Lupe is the _____ tree climber of all. (swift)

12. The tree frogs are _____ than the students expected. (small)

13. Lupe is putting the _____ lens of all on the camera. (large)

14. She is photographing the _____ kind of frog in the state. (rare)

15. The students are _____ now than they were at the beginning of the hike. (happy)

# Part 3

Circle six adjectives that you could use to compare things. Pick one adjective to make up a sentence about frogs. Pick another adjective to make up a sentence about toads.

16. _____

_____

_____

17. _____

_____

_____

| X | S | L | O | U | D | E | S | T |
|---|---|---|---|---|---|---|---|---|
| S | M | O | O | T | H | E | R | Z |
| Z | A | Q | X | B | B | V | B | K |
| X | L | U | C | K | I | E | R | X |
| Q | L | I | Z | M | G | L | D | I |
| Z | E | C | O | Z | G | R | B | Q |
| V | S | K | V | K | E | B | Z | O |
| R | T | E | Z | L | S | X | T | I |
| G | X | R | V | Z | T | L | L | Y |

**Name** _____

Beasts & Critters

# Proofreading
## Practice

Read this report about elephants and find the mistakes. Use the proofreading marks to show how each mistake should be fixed.

### Proofreading Marks

| Mark | Means | Example |
|------|-------|---------|
| ℉ | take away | Please pass ~~the~~ the apples. |
| ∧ | add | Please ^pass^ the apples. |
| ≡ | make into a capital letter | please pass the apples. |
| / | make into a lowercase letter | Please Pass the apples. |
| ⊙ | add a period | Please pass the apples⊙ |
| ⑤ᵖ | fix spelling | Pleaz pass the apples. |

## Learning About Elephants

Me and Paul visited an elephant trainer. She told Paul and I a lot about elephants. She said that elephants are smart. Here are some of the other things we learned.

Every elephant has a trunk, but trunks are all alike. An African elephant's trunk have two fleshy knobs at the tip. An Asian elephant's trunk it has one knob.

An elephant's trunk is powerful and useful. It can lift a log that weighs 600 pounds. It can also pik up a penny.

to bathe, elephants fill their trunks with water and they sprays themselves If an elephant didn't have no trunk, it would get thirsty. They drink with their trunks.

Elephants also use their trunks to communicate. They often touch trunks when they meet. This is an elephant's way Of saying hello

Paul and me enjoyed our visit. Someday we would like to go to Asia or Africa and see some elephants in the wild.

Beasts & Critters

# Proofreading
## Checklist

You can use the list below to help you find and fix mistakes in your own writing. Write the titles of your own stories or reports in the blanks on top of the chart. Then use the questions to check your work. Make a check mark (✓) in each box after you have checked that item.

### Proofreading Checklist for Unit 4

| | Titles | | | |
|---|---|---|---|---|
| Have I used subject pronouns correctly? (*I, you, he, she, it, we, they*) | | | | |
| Have I used *I* and *me* correctly when naming myself and another person? | | | | |
| Do the subject and verb in every sentence agree? | | | | |
| Have I avoided extra pronouns? | | | | |

### Also Remember . . .

| | | | | |
|---|---|---|---|---|
| Does each sentence begin with a capital letter? | | | | |
| Does each sentence end with the right mark? | | | | |
| Have I spelled each word correctly? | | | | |
| Have I used commas correctly? | | | | |

### Your Own List

Use this space to write your own list of things to check in your writing.

| | | | | |
|---|---|---|---|---|
| | | | | |
| | | | | |
| | | | | |

Name _____

Beasts & Critters

# Pronouns

Write the pronoun that could take the place of the underlined word or words in each sentence.

1. <u>Sara and Maria</u> saw a film about green turtles. _____

2. <u>Maria</u> wrote a report on the life cycle of the green turtle. _____

3. Then Maria asked <u>Sara</u> for help. _____

4. Sara drew a picture of <u>green turtles</u> on a beach. _____

5. <u>You and I</u> could learn a lot from Maria's report. _____

For each sentence, choose the correct words in ( ). Write them in the blank.

6. _____ watched the huge dragonfly. (Me and Jerry/Jerry and I)

7. The dragonfly landed on the mat between _____. (Jerry and me/Jerry and I)

8. _____ sat very still to watch the bug. (Jerry and I/I and Jerry)

9. The dragonfly stayed with _____ for five minutes. (me and Jerry/Jerry and me)

Cross out the extra pronoun or the extra negative in each sentence.

10. You do not never want to tease a crocodile.

11. Crocodiles they can break a board in two with their jaws.

12. My brother he cared for crocodiles in a wild animal park.

13. Animal trainers don't teach crocodiles no tricks.

# Verbs

Rewrite each sentence so the underlined verb tells about the past.

14. A fox <u>hunts</u> rats and mice in this field.

_____

15. Those small animals <u>cause</u> problems for the farmer.

_____

_____

Write a word from the pair in ( ) to complete each sentence correctly.

16. Tigers _____ large animals. (hunt/hunts)

17. Tigers _____ very swift. (is/are)

18. That female tiger _____ a very good hunter. (is/are)

19. She _____ very quietly toward her prey. (walk/walks)

# Adjectives

Underline the word or words in ( ) that complete each sentence correctly.

20. Do you know which animal is the (tiniest/most tiny) creature on Earth?

21. The blue whale is the (largest/most large).

22. It is much (heavier/heaviest) than the biggest elephant.

23. Some whales that are (smaller/more small) than the blue whale eat large fish.

24. Are tiny krill the (smaller/smallest) fish of all?

25. Krill must be (biggest/bigger) than something!

Name _____

Beasts & Critters

# School 🏠 Home Connection

In Unit 4 of *G.U.M.* students are learning how different kinds of words are used in sentences. The activities on this sheet give extra practice with some concepts they are studying. You can help your child use the information he or she is learning in school by choosing one or more of these activities to complete with your child at home.

## Word Search  (Verbs and Time)

Circle six verbs in the puzzle.

| | | | | | | | |
|---|---|---|---|---|---|---|---|
| P | Q | Z | T | W | A | A | O |
| L | A | S | P | O | N | Q | R |
| A | B | T | S | R | C | H | A |
| Y | X | O | P | K | R | E | B |
| X | R | P | V | P | A | L | D |
| Y | S | Z | N | N | W | P | R |
| T | R | A | V | E | L | E | D |
| Z | Q | B | F | O | E | D | X |
| A | O | Q | W | X | D | Q | K |

Write the verbs that tell about the present.

_____

_____

Write the verbs that tell about the past.

_____

_____

What ending do all these past tense verbs have? _____

## In the News  (Choosing Subject and Object Pronouns)

Read a magazine or newspaper article together. Help your child circle the pronouns. For each pronoun, ask these questions:

- Is this a subject pronoun or an object pronoun?
- Which word or words does this pronoun take the place of?

| Subject pronouns | *I, you, he, she, it, we, they* |
|---|---|
| Object pronouns | *me, you, him, her, it, us, them* |

## Beasts & Critters

109

## Big, Bigger, Biggest  (Comparing with Adjectives)

Two to six people can play this game. First work with your child to write several word trios on slips of paper. Use the word trios below as examples. Write each trio on a separate slip of paper.

| | | | | | |
|---|---|---|---|---|---|
| big | tall | wide | small | noisy | silly |
| bigger | taller | wider | smaller | noisier | sillier |
| biggest | tallest | widest | smallest | noisiest | silliest |

Put the slips in a hat or bag. Have each player, in turn, draw a slip and think of three things that can be compared using each set of words. Players get a point for each comparison they make.

**Example**   A hippo is **big**.
An elephant is **bigger** than a hippo.
A blue whale is **biggest** of all.

## Scrambler  (Making the Subject and Verb Agree)

Help your child create an original word scramble like the ones below. First, write 3–5 simple sentences about an animal using some of these verbs: *eat/eats, live/lives, like/likes, hunt/hunts,* and *sleep/sleeps*. Then rewrite the sentences on a separate sheet of paper and replace the verb in each sentence with blank lines, one line for each letter in the missing verb. Scramble the letters in the verb and add them to the end of the sentence in  parentheses. Encourage your child to share the word scramble with friends or family members.

**Example**    Some monkeys ___ ___ ___ ___ in trees. (eilv)

Most monkeys ___ ___ ___ ___ to play. (kile)

A monkey ___ ___ ___ ___ fruits and insects. (taes)

Name  _____

Beasts & Critters

Can an earthquake cause damage?
what is an earthquake.

**The first sentence is written correctly. Circle two mistakes in the second sentence. Rewrite this sentence correctly.**

_____

Begin each sentence with a **capital letter**. Put a **period** at the end of a telling sentence and a command. Put a **question mark** at the end of an asking sentence. Put an **exclamation point** at the end of a sentence that shows strong feelings.

See Handbook  Sections 1, 6, and 9

# Part 1

Circle each letter that should be a capital letter in the sentences below. Add a punctuation mark at the end of each sentence.

1. beneath the land and the oceans are large layers of rock____

2. These layers of rock are called plates____

3. the plates move against each other____

4. What happens when the plates squeeze together____

5. the ground rolls and shakes____

6. sometimes cracks form

   on Earth's surface____

7. Many earthquakes happen

   where two plates meet____

**Earthquakes are caused when plates shift and move.**

8. Look for a map of Earth's plates in a world atlas____

# Part 2
**Rewrite each sentence correctly.**

9. what should I do during an earthquake _____

_____

10. you should go under a desk _____

11. wow, the room really shook _____

12. quick, get under this table _____

13. may I get up now _____

14. wait until someone tells you it's safe _____

_____

15. the shaking has stopped, so we can stand up _____

_____

# Part 3
**Draw a line from each sentence on the left to the words on the right that tell about the sentence.**

| | |
|---|---|
| 16. Hurrah, the earthquake has ended! | tells something |
| 17. How can you be ready for an earthquake? | gives a command |
| 18. It's a good idea to have water, a flashlight, and a battery-powered radio. | asks something |
| 19. Be calm. | shows strong emotion |

**Name** _____

The World Outside

112

# Read and Discover

On May 18, 1980, a **volcano** erupted near the city of **toutle**, in Washington. A **man** named **bruce nelson** saw the volcano erupt.

Underline each word in bold type that should start with a capital letter.

**Proper nouns** are the names of particular people, places, or things. **Capitalize** a person's first and last name. **Capitalize** each important word in the names of streets, towns, countries, parks, rivers, oceans, mountains, and lakes.

See Handbook  Sections 1 and 13

# Part 1

Circle the words in bold type that should begin with a capital letter.

My mom's friend **karen** saw ash and **smoke**

shoot out of **mount st. helens**. Her sister,

**ann**, had to leave home. **Mr. knox** heard

that their **town**, **yakima**, was in danger.

The **family** left for **seattle** quickly.

**Mount St. Helens blew its top in 1980.**

This eruption was the first in the continental United States outside of **alaska**

since 1921. That **year mt. lassen**, a **peak** in northern California, erupted.

**Now write each name you circled. Use capital letters correctly.**

1. _____    5. _____

2. _____    6. _____

3. _____    7. _____

4. _____    8. _____

The World Outside

113

# Part 2

**Rewrite the paragraph below. Begin each proper noun with a capital letter.**

On april 18, 1906, a huge earthquake shook san francisco. Many buildings fell down. Fires burned from San francisco bay to van ness avenue. Many families set up tents in golden gate park.

_____

_____

_____

_____

# Part 3

This chart shows some active volcanoes in the United States. Use the information to write a sentence about one volcano. Remember to capitalize proper nouns.

| State | Volcano | Height (in feet) |
|---|---|---|
| Hawaii | Mauna Loa | 13,681 |
| Alaska | Mt. Wrangell | 14,163 |
| Washington | Mount St. Helens | 8,363 |

_____

_____

_____

_____

Name _____

The World Outside

Doctor Mary Lee Coogan went to Yosemite National Park.
Dr. M.L. Coogan climbed Half Dome.

Which letters in the second sentence stand for names? _____
What punctuation mark is used after each letter? _____
Which word in the first sentence is written in a shorter way in the
second sentence? _____ What punctuation mark is used
with it? _____

**Abbreviations** are short forms of words. An abbreviation usually begins with a capital letter and ends with a period. A **title of respect** (like *Doctor*) is used before a person's name. Many titles of respect are written as abbreviations (*Dr.*). An **initial** can take the place of a name. It is written as a capital letter followed by a period.

**See Handbook  Sections 1 and 2**

# Part 1

Write each underlined word as an abbreviation. Write underlined initials correctly.

1. <u>Doctor</u> Chan told us about President Theodore Roosevelt. _____

2. Many people called Roosevelt by his initials, <u>t r</u>. _____

3. Roosevelt lived at 1600 Pennsylvania <u>Avenue</u>. _____

4. That is the address of the White House in

   Washington, <u>District of Columbia</u>. _____

5. Roosevelt protected forests in the

   <u>United States of America</u>. _____

**President Roosevelt protected 148 million acres of forest land.**

6. <u>Mister</u> Roosevelt also created the first national wildlife refuge. _____

7. It is on Pelican Island. My aunt, <u>Mistress</u> Lee, lives near there. _____

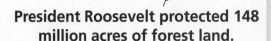

# Part 2

Write names of people or things. Use an abbreviation with each.

8. the name of a doctor _____

9. the name of a man you know _____

10. the name of a woman you know _____

11. the name of a street near your school _____

12. the name of a street near your home _____

# Part 3

Write the correct abbreviation or initial for each underlined word.

13. <u>Doctor</u> <u>Wilma</u> Reynolds   [__]__. __. Reynolds

14. Señora <u>Elena</u> Cordero   Señora [__]. Cordero

15. <u>North</u> Sycamore <u>Street</u>   [__].Sycamore __ __.

16. Miller <u>Avenue</u>   Miller [__]__ __.

17. <u>Mister</u> <u>Lee</u> Kwan   __ __.[__].Kwan

18. <u>Isabel</u> Criado   [__].Criado

Write the letters in the boxes in order to complete the name of the national park in the sentence below.

Mt. McKinley is located in ___ ___ ___ ___ ___ ___ National Park.

Name _____

The World Outside

Amy read a book titled <u>The Sun and Stars</u>.
Bill read a book called planet earth.

**Underline the title of the book in the second sentence. Circle the letters that should be capital letters.**

**Capitalize** the first word, the last word, and all the important words in a **title** of a book. Verbs such as *is* and *are* are important words. Always **underline** a book title or use *italic type* if you are writing with a word processor.

See Handbook Sections 1 and 3

# Part 1

Underline each book title. Cross out each small letter that needs to be a capital. Write the capital letter above it.

1. Dr. Lee wrote a book titled what fossils tell us.

2. Have you read the book the lava caves?

3. Sheila checked out a book called earthquakes.

4. Joan saw a book titled exploring safely.

5. In the library, I looked at a book called how mountains are made.

6. Do you know who wrote the book mississippi floods?

7. I want to read the book titled the volcanoes of hawaii.

8. Lupe's mother wrote a book called make your home safe.

9. The book titled mountains of ice is about glaciers.

10. Rashad bought the book called tornado chasers for his sister.

The World Outside

# Part 2

Write the title of a book below that best completes each sentence. Underline each title correctly and use capital letters where they belong.

**sandstorm in the desert**

**rooms inside the earth**     **flood on the ohio river**

**how to control forest fires**     **the blizzard of 2007**

11. The book called _____ is probably about caves.

12. If you want to learn about fire safety, read _____.

13. If you like to read about snowstorms, you might like the book called _____

    _____.

14. A river that overflowed is described in _____.

15. The book called _____ tells about a kind of

    weather event that happens in dry areas.

# Part 3

You're an author! Write the title of a book you would like to write. Next, write a sentence telling what the book is about. Include the title of your book in the sentence. Then write your sentence using a word processor. Use italic type for the title of your book.

_____

_____

_____

Name _____

The World Outside

# Read and Discover

Yellowstone National Park is America's oldest park. **Find the word that means "belonging to America." Make the punctuation mark used in this word. ___ Is *America* singular or plural? _____ What letter follows the punctuation mark? ___**

Bears sometimes approach tourists' cars there. **Find the word that means "belonging to tourists." Make the punctuation mark used in this word. ___ Is *tourists* singular or plural? _____ Is there an *s* after this punctuation mark? _____**

A **possessive noun** shows what someone owns or what something has. Add an apostrophe and *s* to a singular noun to show possession (*Joe's book; Bess's book*). Add an apostrophe after the *s* of a plural noun that ends in *s* (*girls' books*). Add an apostrophe and *s* if a plural noun doesn't end in *s* (*women's books*).

**See Handbook** Sections 7 and 24

# Part 1

**Underline the correct possessive form in each sentence.**

1. Geysers are (nature's/natures's) fountains.

2. A (geyser'/geyser's) spray is very hot.

3. The water comes from beneath (Earth's/Earths') surface.

4. Tourists want to see (Yellowstones'/Yellowstone's) geysers.

5. This (parks/park's) most famous geyser is Old Faithful.

6. About every hour, water shoots out of (Old Faithful's/Old Faithfuls') mouth.

7. Can you hear the clicks of hundreds of (visitor's/visitors') cameras?

**Old Faithful shoots water 100 feet in the air.**

The World Outside

## Part 2

Rewrite each underlined phrase. Make one word a possessive.

8. Reggie is using <u>the phone that belongs to his sisters</u>. _____

    _____

9. He was invited to go to Yellowstone with <u>the family of his friend</u>.

    _____

10. Reggie will borrow <u>a sleeping bag from his brother</u>. _____

    _____

11. He is writing down <u>the addresses of his friends</u>. _____

    _____

12. He will buy postcards at <u>the gift shop in Yellowstone</u>. _____

    _____

## Part 3

Imagine that you're going to visit Yellowstone. Think of three things you might borrow for the trip. Complete each sentence by writing a possessive expression.

13. I would borrow my _____.

14. I would borrow my _____.

15. I would borrow my _____.

Name _____

The World Outside

# Read and Discover

**We are** studying the Danakil Desert in Africa.
**We're** learning about the harsh environment there.

Look at the words in bold type in each sentence.
Do they have the same meaning, or a different meaning?
_____ What letter is left out of *we're*? _____
What mark replaces this letter? _____

A **contraction** is made of two words put together. An **apostrophe** takes the place of one or more letters in a contraction.

| | | |
|---|---|---|
| *I + am = I'm* | *is + not = isn't* | *are + not = aren't* |
| *we + have = we've* | *you + will = you'll* | *she + is = she's* |

**See Handbook** Sections 7 and 22

# Part 1

Circle each contraction. Write the words that were joined to make the contraction.

1. The Danakil Desert doesn't have a mild climate. _____

2. It's one of the hottest, driest places on Earth. _____

3. You'll never guess that it used to lie at the bottom of the sea. _____

4. The sea isn't there anymore, but when it dried it left a shallow lake and tons

   of salt. _____

5. I've read that the salt deposits look like snow. _____

6. Don't miners gather the salt to sell? _____

7. Some huts look like snow houses, but they aren't made of snow. _____

8. They're made out of salt bricks! _____

The World Outside

# Part 2

Rewrite the underlined words in each sentence as a contraction.

9. Alicia and I sometimes pretend that <u>we are</u> traveling across the Danakil

   Desert. _____

10. We <u>could not</u> get very far without supplies. _____

11. <u>She will</u> pack bottles of water. _____

12. <u>I am</u> in charge of food and the tent. _____

13. When we get to the salt deposits, we <u>cannot</u> see anything but white.

    _____

14. <u>We have</u> traveled as far as we can go. _____

# Part 3

On each knot below, write a contraction that is formed using the word *not*.
Can you tie all nine "nots"?

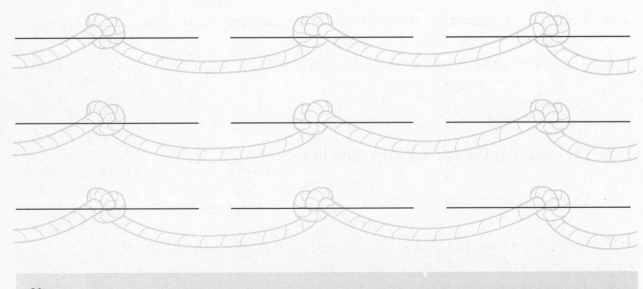

Name _____

The World Outside

The cave was dark, damp, and quiet.
Cave explorers found rocks minerals and water inside.

How many commas are in the first sentence? _____
Draw a star in two places in the second sentence where a comma belongs.

A **series** is a list of three or more words. Use **commas** to separate words in a series.

See Handbook  Section 8

# Part 1

Add commas where they are needed in these sentences. Write *C* next to each sentence that uses commas correctly.

1. Rainwater, lava, and ocean waves form different kinds of caves. ___

2. Underground rivers waterfalls and lakes can be found inside some caves. ___

3. My uncle and aunt have explored caves

   made of limestone marble and dolomite. ___

4. Inside one cave we saw bats spiders, and lizards. ___

5. We found some algae, ferns, and mosses

   growing near the cave opening. ___

6. In a cave where ancient people lived,

   you might find stone tools,

   wall paintings, and animal bones. ___

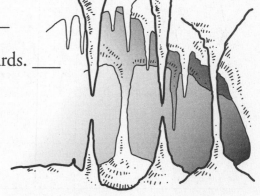

**Cones that hang from the ceiling of a cave are stalactites. Cones that rise from the floor are stalagmites.**

7. A guide will give you a flashlight, a pen a notebook and a map. ___

8. Please stay close to Sadako Janet and me. ___

# Part 2

A cave explorer was taking notes. She dropped her flashlight and had to write in the dark. Read her notes and add commas where they are needed.

Today I found the most amazing plants minerals and animals. There were beautiful flowers small bushes and lush ferns just outside the cave's opening. Inside the cave, I came across many interesting rocks, such as sandstone quartz and obsidian. I also saw many beetles salamanders worms and lizards crawling about.

# Part 3

Try to find all six words in the Cave Word Search below. Write a sentence listing all the things you found in the cave.

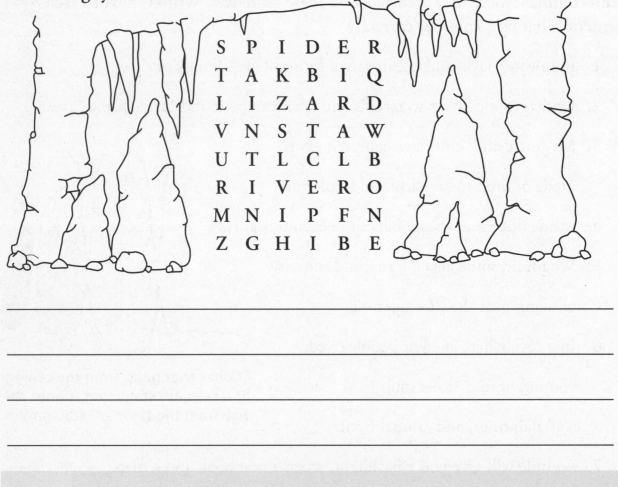

```
S P I D E R
T A K B I Q
L I Z A R D
V N S T A W
U T L C L B
R I V E R O
M N I P F N
Z G H I B E
```

_____

_____

_____

_____

Name _____

The World Outside

# Read and Discover

Yes, Hawaii is a group of volcanic islands.
**Circle the word that makes this sentence sound like an answer to
a question. What punctuation mark follows that word? _____**

No most of Hawaii's volcanoes do not erupt often.
**Circle the word that makes this sentence sound like an answer.
Add the missing comma.**

Use a **comma** to show a pause in a sentence. Write a comma after
the words *yes* and *no* when they begin a sentence.

See Handbook Section 8

## Part 1

Add a comma to each answer.

1. Does Hawaii have active volcanoes? Yes Hawaii does.

2. Is Hawaii dangerous to visit? No you can visit Hawaii safely.

3. Did the islands rise up from the sea? Yes they were built up by eruptions.

4. Will the islands of Hawaii stay the same size forever?

   No the islands will continue to change size.

5. Is Mauna Loa the world's tallest volcano?

   Yes it rises almost 30,000 feet

   above the ocean floor.

6. Does the lava from Mauna Loa

   always flow out of the top?

   No sometimes lava comes out the sides.

**Mauna Loa is on the big
island of Hawaii, the largest
of the Hawaiian Islands.**

# Part 2

Answer each question. Begin each sentence with *Yes* or *No* and a comma.

7. Have you seen pictures of Hawaii? _____

8. Do you live near a volcano? _____

9. Would you like to visit an active volcano? _____

_____

10. Do you think volcanic eruptions are exciting? _____

11. Do you know why volcanoes erupt? _____

_____

12. Do you think lava is dangerous? _____

# Part 3

Add a comma to each answer. Then make up a silly question about volcanoes to go with it. Share your questions and answers with a friend.

| Questions | Answers |
|---|---|
| Do volcanoes erupt in your kitchen? | Yes, they do it every day of the week. |
| _____ | No that would be too dangerous. |
| _____ | Yes I really liked that. |
| _____ | No I don't think that is a good idea. |
| _____ | |

Name _____

The World Outside

My uncle said, "Next month I will travel to Antarctica." Underline the speaker's words in this sentence. Circle the quotation marks that come before and after the statement.

What will you do there? I asked. Underline the speaker's words in this sentence. Draw a star in two places in this sentence where you think quotation marks belong.

Use **quotation marks** to show someone's exact written or spoken words. Quotation marks go around the beginning and end of a **direct quotation**. Do not use quotation marks when the word *that* comes before someone's words.

See Handbook Section 4

# Part 1

Add quotation marks to the sentences that need them. Write *C* next to each sentence that does not need quotation marks.

1. My uncle told me that he will work at a research station in Antarctica. ___

2. Antarctica is the coldest place on Earth, he said. ___

3. He explained that it is the icy continent at the South Pole. ___

4. He said that the world's lowest temperature was recorded there. ___

5. It was −128.6°F in July 1983, he said. ___

6. Thick ice covers most of the land, said my uncle. ___

7. He said, Over millions of years, layers of snow

   pressed together to form a huge icecap. ___

8. He said that the ice has been more than 15,700 feet thick. ___

9. That's ten times the height of the tallest building! I said. ___

Emperor penguins live in Antarctica.

# Part 2

Rewrite the sentences. Add quotation marks around the speakers' exact words.

10. Why are you going to such a cold place? I asked. _____

    _____

11. He answered, I will study Antarctica's largest land animal. _____

    _____

12. Is it a polar bear? I asked. _____

13. No, polar bears live near the North Pole, he answered. _____

    _____

14. He said, The largest land animal that lives in Antarctica permanently is an
    insect that's half an inch long.

    _____

    _____

# Part 3

Imagine you are planning an expedition to Antarctica. Write a conversation
between you and a friend about your trip. Remember to use quotation marks.

_____

_____

_____

Name _____

The World Outside

a. Mark shouted, "Let's hike across the glacier!"
b. "Be careful where you step! Jill cried.

**Which sentence is written correctly?** _____
**Circle where something is missing in the other sentence.**

A **direct quotation** shows a speaker's exact words. Use a comma to separate the quotation from the rest of the sentence. Put **quotation marks** around a direct quotation. Add punctuation before the last quotation mark.
<u>Examples</u>
"Look out!" Mark cried.
"Why?" Jill asked.
"The ice is slippery," Mark answered.

See Handbook Sections 4 and 8

# Part 1

Write *C* next to each sentence that uses punctuation marks correctly. Add punctuation marks when you need to.

1. Peter said, "The glacier is made of ice, and it's

   moving very slowly toward the sea." ___

2. Wendy asked "What happens after the

   glacier passes ___

   **Icebergs break off glaciers in a process called calving.**

3. Peter replied, "Glaciers can leave behind lakes, valleys, and hills" ___

4. "Some glaciers are so big they reach all the way to the sea" Peter added. ___

5. Wendy said "Look, I can see whales swimming near that glacier!" ___

6. Did you know that when parts of a glacier break off and float out to sea, they

   are called icebergs? asked Wendy. ___

**The World Outside**

129

# Part 2

Rewrite each sentence as a direct quotation.

7. Martha said that much of Earth was covered with ice long ago. _____

_____

8. James explained that the animals were forced southward by the ice. _____

_____

_____

9. Tisha asked what happened when the ice started to melt. _____

_____

10. Martha told Tisha that the animals were able to move back to the north.

_____

_____

# Part 3

Rewrite this conversation. Add missing punctuation marks. Start a new paragraph with each change in speaker.

There is an iceberg in our path! Stop the ship shouted the first mate. Let's go around it said the captain. We already have enough ice.

_____

_____

_____

Name _____

The World Outside

# Proofreading
## Practice

Read this report about erosion and find the mistakes. Use the proofreading marks to show how each mistake should be fixed.

### Proofreading Marks

| Mark | Means | Example |
|------|-------|---------|
| ⊙ | add a period | She said, "I'm here⊙ |
| ∧ | add a comma | She said∧ "I'm here." |
| ⌄ | add quotation marks | She said, ⌄I'm here.⌄ |
| ⌄ | add an apostrophe | She said, "I⌄m here." |
| ≡ | make into a capital letter | ≡she said, "I'm here." |
| ௨ | take away | She ௨said, "I'm here." |
| (sp) | fix spelling | She said, "I'm hear.(sp)" |

## Erosion

Were studying natural forces in Mr. Hom's science class. A scientist named

Dr. e.m Cody came to talk to hour class. She's an expert on erosion.

Erosion is a natural process that slowly changes the lands surface every day. Wind,

ice, and water wear away pieces of rock and soil and carry them away.

Mr Hom showed us Dr. Cody's book about erosion. It's called mountains into

molehills. He asked Dr. Cody to talk awhile and answer students questions.

"Erosion crumbles mountains and carves out canyons," Dr. Cody told us. She

said that the colorado River created the Grand Canyon by wearing away rock.

"Could the river behind my house be at the bottom of a canyon someday asked Bo.

"Yes" Dr. Cody explained. "but it would take thousands of years"

Next week we're going to Bryce Canyon. erosion there has created valleys filled

with spikes of rock shaped like towers castles and animals. I cant wait to go!

# Proofreading
## Checklist

You can use the list below to help you find and fix mistakes in your own writing. Write the titles of your own stories or reports in the blanks on top of the chart. Then use the questions to check your work. Make a check mark (✓) in each box after you have checked that item.

**Titles**

### Proofreading Checklist for Unit 5

| | | | | |
|---|---|---|---|---|
| Does each sentence begin with a capital letter and end with the right mark? | | | | |
| Do all proper names and important words in a title begin with a capital letter? | | | | |
| Have I placed quotation marks around each speaker's words? | | | | |
| Have I used possessives correctly? | | | | |
| Have I used contractions correctly? | | | | |

### Also Remember . . .

| | | | | |
|---|---|---|---|---|
| Do commas separate each item in a list? | | | | |
| Do all abbreviations begin with a capital letter and end with a period? | | | | |

### Your Own List

Use this space to write your own list of things to check in your writing.

| | | | | |
|---|---|---|---|---|
| | | | | |
| | | | | |
| | | | | |

**Name** _____

The World Outside

# Review

## Sentences

Rewrite each sentence correctly.

1. scientists chip away bits of rock. _____

2. look, I found seashells in this rock _____

   _____

3. was this entire area once covered by the ocean _____

   _____

4. yes sea animals lived here millions of years ago _____

   _____

## Proper Nouns and Book Titles

Circle each letter that needs to be a capital letter.

5. my favorite book is called <u>life on the mesa</u>.

6. mesas are found in arizona, new mexico, colorado, and utah.

7. i hiked in colorado's mesa verde national park with mrs. joseph.

8. she gave me <u>the red mountain</u>, another book about mesas.

## Quotation Marks

Add quotation marks around the speakers' exact words.

9. Noel said, Let's go to Carlsbad Caverns.

10. Michael exclaimed, Inside the caves some rocks look like upside-down trees!

The World Outside

# Quotations and Possessives

**Add quotation marks, commas, and periods to make each sentence correct.**

11. Debbi said All the regions of Earth lie atop minerals

12. She added "Minerals are used to make pencils, nickels, and salt"

13. Barry said, Scientists learned that minerals grow by adding layers of crystals

**Circle the word in ( ) that correctly completes each sentence.**

14. Some of (Earths'/Earth's) changes happen over a long period of time.

15. (Continents/Continents') shapes slowly change as plates under the crust shift.

16. The (plate's/plates') movements cause earthquakes on the surface of Earth.

17. (Earth's/Earths) core is filled with hot bubbling rock.

# Contractions

**Write the word in ( ) that best completes each sentence.**

18. Tidal waves _____ caused by tides. (arent/aren't)

19. _____ caused by earthquakes under water. (They're/Theyre')

20. _____ learn about these huge waves, called tsunamis. (Well/We'll)

21. _____ seen waves that were 50 feet high. (Hes/He's)

# Commas

**Add commas where they are needed.**

22. Yes rocks are useful.

23. Many buildings are made of granite marble or limestone.

24. No you couldn't make a car out of rock.

25. Maria Jack and I searched for smooth rocks in the riverbed.

Name _____

The World Outside

# School 🏫 Home Connection

In Unit 5 of *G.U.M.* students are learning which letters to capitalize and how to use punctuation marks. The activities on this page give extra practice with some of the concepts in the unit. You can help your child use the information he or she is learning by choosing one or more activities to complete with your child at home.

**Crossword Puzzle (Writing Sentences Correctly; Commas in a Series; Showing Ownership; Contractions; Direct Quotations)**

Work with your child to complete the puzzle.

**Across**

1. These marks come at the __ of a sentence. (? . !)
4. This mark separates items in a list.
5. The apostrophe in *I've* stands for two missing __.
6. Sentences always begin with this kind of letter.
7. This kind of sentence ends with a question mark.
8. You must capitalize the first letter of each important word in a __.

**Down**

1. Sentences showing strong feeling end with this kind of mark.
2. This kind of word is made of two words joined together with an apostrophe.
3. This kind of sentence ends with a period.
9. Quotation marks belong around a speaker's __ words.

## Where Are You? (Proper Nouns; Initials and Abbreviations)

Help your child write exactly where you live.

| Example | North America, U.S.A., N.Y., New York City, Manhattan, Greenwich Village, Hudson St. |

Tell your child to use abbreviations where appropriate and make sure to capitalize place names. Try doing the same exercise for other locations familiar to your child, such as a grandparent's home or your child's school.

## Long, Long Lists (Commas in a Series)

Ask your child to write a sentence that lists several favorite foods or games. Remind him or her to use commas to separate items.

| Example | I love ice cream, tacos, grapes, oranges, and pizza. |

Other family members might enjoy thinking up new topics for lists and seeing who can write the longest sentence.

## I Said/You Said (Writing Quotations)

Ask your child to write down a conversation you recently had together. Ask him or her to use quotation marks and to include the identity of the speaker in each line.

| Example | I said, "I'd like a carrot."<br>"There's one on the table for you," Dad said. |

Without reading your child's record of the conversation, write the dialogue down as you remember it. Compare the two. Discuss with your child how your memories are different.

## All-Time Favorites (Book Titles)

Ask your child to write the titles of three books he or she has greatly enjoyed reading. Tell your child to be sure to underline each title and capitalize the first letter of all the important words in it.

Name _____

The World Outside

# Appendix Table of Contents

**TEST TIP:** Be sure to read all of the answer choices before deciding on an answer.

Read each item carefully. Select the best answer. Fill in the circle on the answer sheet below.

1. **Which of the following is a complete sentence?**

   A  Athletes in ancient Greece.
   B  Came to a stadium in Nemea.
   C  They competed in athletic events.
   D  The first Olympic Games.

2. **Read this sentence.**

   The Olympic Games began in ancient Greece.

   **Which is the subject of the sentence?**

   A  the Olympic
   B  the Olympic Games
   C  Olympic Games began
   D  began in ancient Greece

3. **Read this sentence.**

   Ancient books described the events.

   **Which is the predicate of the sentence?**

   A  ancient books
   B  books described
   C  books described the events
   D  described the events

4. **Read these sentences.**

   Only men could compete in the events. Was this fair to women?

   **Which statement tells about the sentences?**

   A  The first sentence is a telling sentence, and the second is an asking sentence.

   B  Both sentences are telling sentences.
   C  The first sentence is an asking sentence, and the second is a telling sentence.
   D  Both sentences are asking sentences.

5. **Read these sentences.**

   Run two laps around the track. What a swift runner you are!

   **Which statement tells about the sentences?**

   A  The first sentence shows strong feeling, and the second gives a command.
   B  Both sentences show strong feeling.
   C  The first sentence gives a command, and the second shows strong feeling.
   D  Both sentences give commands.

**Example:**

● Ⓑ Ⓒ Ⓓ

**Answer Sheet**

1. Ⓐ Ⓑ Ⓒ Ⓓ
2. Ⓐ Ⓑ Ⓒ Ⓓ
3. Ⓐ Ⓑ Ⓒ Ⓓ
4. Ⓐ Ⓑ Ⓒ Ⓓ
5. Ⓐ Ⓑ Ⓒ Ⓓ

Read each item carefully. Select the best answer. Fill in the circle on the answer sheet below.

6. Read this sentence.

   English settlers **founded** Salem, Massachusetts, in 1626.

   **Which words are a prepositional phrase that tells** *how, when,* **or** *where* **about the word in bold type?**

   A English settlers
   B Salem, Massachusetts
   C in 1626
   D 1626

7. **Which item below is a fragment?**

   A The word *salem* means "peace."
   B Salem has a good harbor.
   C Fishermen caught loads of codfish.
   D Dried the fish on wood racks.

8. **Which sentence gives the most information?**

   A Ships carried cargo from Salem to other places.
   B Sailing ships carried the dried cod from Salem to distant lands.
   C Sailing ships sailed to distant lands.
   D Ships sailed from Salem with a lot of dried cod.

9. **Which sentence is a correctly written compound sentence?**

   A The sailors scrub the deck and polish the brass.
   B The captain gives orders the sailors scrub the deck.
   C The captain and the sailors give orders and polish the brass.
   D The captain gives orders, and the sailors scrub the deck.

10. **Read this sentence.**

    Ships brought silks and spices back to Salem merchants sold these goods for high prices.

    **How should this sentence be rewritten?**

    A Add a comma and a joining word.
    B Add a subject.
    C Add a predicate.
    D It should not be rewritten. It is written correctly.

**Answer Sheet**

6. Ⓐ Ⓑ Ⓒ Ⓓ
7. Ⓐ Ⓑ Ⓒ Ⓓ
8. Ⓐ Ⓑ Ⓒ Ⓓ
9. Ⓐ Ⓑ Ⓒ Ⓓ
10. Ⓐ Ⓑ Ⓒ Ⓓ

Read each item carefully. Select the best answer. Fill in the circle on the answer sheet below.

11. **Which of the following is a complete sentence?**

    A  Taos Pueblo in New Mexico.
    B  Adobe buildings with thick walls.
    C  Adobe is made from dirt, water, and straw.
    D  Poured or formed into bricks.

12. **Read this sentence.**

    Many artists have painted pictures of Taos Pueblo.

    **What is the subject of the sentence?**

    A  many
    B  many artists
    C  artists have painted
    D  pictures of Taos Pueblo

13. **Read this sentence.**

    Some buildings have no doors.

    **What is the predicate of the sentence?**

    A  some
    B  some buildings
    C  buildings have
    D  have no doors

14. **Read these sentences.**

    How could people enter a building with no doors? A hole in the top was the entrance.

    **Which statement tells about the sentences?**

    A  The first sentence is a telling sentence, and the second is an asking sentence.

    B  Both sentences are telling sentences.

    C  The first sentence is an asking sentence, and the second is a telling sentence.

    D  Both sentences are asking sentences.

15. **Read these sentences.**

    How beautiful the Taos Pueblo is! Take a photograph of the adobe bricks.

    **Which statement tells about the sentences?**

    A  The first sentence shows strong feeling, and the second gives a command.

    B  Both sentences show strong feeling.

    C  The first sentence gives a command, and the second shows strong feeling.

    D  Both sentences give commands.

| **Answer Sheet** | | | |
|---|---|---|---|
| 11. Ⓐ | Ⓑ | Ⓒ | Ⓓ |
| 12. Ⓐ | Ⓑ | Ⓒ | Ⓓ |
| 13. Ⓐ | Ⓑ | Ⓒ | Ⓓ |
| 14. Ⓐ | Ⓑ | Ⓒ | Ⓓ |
| 15. Ⓐ | Ⓑ | Ⓒ | Ⓓ |

Read each item carefully. Select the best answer. Fill in the circle on the answer sheet below.

16. Read this sentence.

    The circus **performs** in an unusual building.

    **Which words are a prepositional phrase that tells *how, when,* or *where* about the word in bold type?**

    A  the circus
    B  in an
    C  in an unusual building
    D  an unusual building

17. **Which item below is a fragment?**

    A  The Moscow Circus is world-famous.
    B  This circus once had more than 4,000 performers.
    C  Traveled throughout the country for many years.
    D  The circus bear was a crowd favorite.

18. **Which sentence gives the most information?**

    A  A tightrope walker strolled on a wire above the crowd.
    B  A person walked on a wire.
    C  A performer walked on a wire that was high in the air.
    D  A performer strolled above the crowd.

19. **Which sentence is a correctly written compound sentence?**

    A  Silly clowns run around the ring and wave to the crowd.
    B  Silly clowns run around the ring a lion jumps on the platform.
    C  Silly clowns and a lion run around the ring and jump on the platform.
    D  Silly clowns run around the ring, and a lion jumps on the platform.

20. Read this sentence.

    A woman balanced on a horse a man lifted a heavy weight.

    **How should this sentence be rewritten?**

    A  Add a comma and a joining word.
    B  Add a subject.
    C  Add a predicate.
    D  It should not be rewritten. It is written correctly.

| Answer Sheet |
| --- |
| 16. (A) (B) (C) (D) |
| 17. (A) (B) (C) (D) |
| 18. (A) (B) (C) (D) |
| 19. (A) (B) (C) (D) |
| 20. (A) (B) (C) (D) |

**TEST TIP:** Fill in only one answer choice for each question.

ardized Test
Format

Read each item carefully. Select the best answer. Fill in the circle on the answer sheet below.

1. **Which of the following sentences has a noun underlined?**

   A  Few sports <u>have</u> one inventor.
   B  Most <u>sports</u> develop over time.
   C  <u>Some</u> events started in ancient times.
   D  Extreme sports are <u>very</u> new.

2. **Which of the following sentences has a proper noun underlined?**

   A  In 1902 a <u>newspaper</u> printed a drawing.
   B  It showed <u>President Theodore Roosevelt</u> and a bear cub.
   C  A man named Morris Michtom saw the <u>cartoon</u>.
   D  He made a <u>stuffed bear</u> called Teddy's Bear to sell.

3. **Which of the following sentences has a plural noun circled?**

   A  Some (companies) invent robots.
   B  This (robot) cleans our home.
   C  Its (brush) sweeps up dirt.
   D  Its (hose) picks up crumbs.

4. **Read this sentence.**

   Are you interested in new inventions?

   **Which word in the sentence is a pronoun?**

   A  are
   B  you
   C  new
   D  inventions

5. **Read this sentence.**

   "That is a wonderful invention!" said Tad.

   **Which word in the sentence is a pronoun?**

   A  that
   B  is
   C  said
   D  Tad

**Example:**

● Ⓑ Ⓒ Ⓓ

**Answer Sheet**

1. Ⓐ Ⓑ Ⓒ Ⓓ
2. Ⓐ Ⓑ Ⓒ Ⓓ
3. Ⓐ Ⓑ Ⓒ Ⓓ
4. Ⓐ Ⓑ Ⓒ Ⓓ
5. Ⓐ Ⓑ Ⓒ Ⓓ

Read each item carefully. Select the best answer. Fill in the circle on the answer sheet below.

6. Which of the following sentences has an action verb underlined?

   A Orville and Wilbur Wright <u>loved</u> machines.
   B In 1902 the Wright brothers made a <u>glider</u>.
   C They tested it in the air <u>nearly</u> 1,000 times.
   D Then they built an <u>airplane</u>.

7. Which of the following sentences has a past tense verb underlined?

   A Many people <u>use</u> ball-point pens today.
   B John H. Loud <u>invented</u> this type of pen in 1888.
   C Modern ball-point pens generally <u>work</u> well.
   D Lazlo Biro <u>gets</u> credit for the improvement of Loud's invention.

8. Which of the following sentences has a linking verb underlined?

   A Margaret Knight <u>invented</u> many things.
   B One invention <u>made</u> special paper bags.
   C These bags <u>had</u> flat bottoms.
   D Bags with flat bottoms <u>are</u> very useful!

9. Read this sentence.

   The dishwasher is a useful machine.

   Which of these words is an adjective in the sentence?

   A dishwasher
   B is
   C useful
   D machine

10. Read this sentence.

   John Fitch and Robert Fulton built early steamboats.

   Which word in the sentence is a joining word?

   A and
   B built
   C early
   D steamboats

**Answer Sheet**

6. Ⓐ Ⓑ Ⓒ Ⓓ
7. Ⓐ Ⓑ Ⓒ Ⓓ
8. Ⓐ Ⓑ Ⓒ Ⓓ
9. Ⓐ Ⓑ Ⓒ Ⓓ
10. Ⓐ Ⓑ Ⓒ Ⓓ

Read each item carefully. Select the best answer. Fill in the circle on the answer sheet below.

11. **Which of the following sentences has a noun underlined?**

    A  People <u>invent</u> games all the time.
    B  <u>Some</u> of these become popular.
    C  Developers create <u>new</u> video games.
    D  Fans love new <u>features</u>.

12. **Which of the following sentences has a proper noun underlined?**

    A  <u>Roller skates</u> are so much fun!
    B  Joseph Merlin <u>invented</u> a type in 1759.
    C  He wore the skates to a party in <u>Belgium</u>.
    D  He had an <u>accident</u> because he didn't know how to stop.

13. **Which of the following sentences has a plural noun circled?**

    A  A good cook invents new (dishes).
    B  My (father) makes odd pancakes.
    C  These pancakes have (mustard) in them!
    D  Dad wraps a (pancake) around a hot dog.

14. **Read this sentence.**

    Inventors give us new ways to do things.

    **Which word in the sentence is a pronoun?**

    A  inventors
    B  us
    C  new
    D  things

15. **Read this sentence.**

    "Did Thomas Edison invent those?" asked Dana.

    **Which word in the sentence is a pronoun?**

    A  did
    B  those
    C  asked
    D  Dana

| **Answer Sheet** | | | |
|---|---|---|---|
| 11. Ⓐ | Ⓑ | Ⓒ | Ⓓ |
| 12. Ⓐ | Ⓑ | Ⓒ | Ⓓ |
| 13. Ⓐ | Ⓑ | Ⓒ | Ⓓ |
| 14. Ⓐ | Ⓑ | Ⓒ | Ⓓ |
| 15. Ⓐ | Ⓑ | Ⓒ | Ⓓ |

Read each item carefully. Select the best answer. Fill in the circle on the answer sheet below.

16. **Which of the following sentences has an action verb underlined?**

    A  Noah Webster produced America's <u>first</u> dictionary.
    B  He published <u>it</u> in 1828.
    C  He <u>wrote</u> short, clear definitions for words.
    D  His <u>dictionary</u> helped students greatly.

17. **Which of the following sentences has a past tense verb underlined?**

    A  People all over the world <u>ride</u> bicycles.
    B  Modern bicycles <u>make</u> travel easy.
    C  Kirkpatrick MacMillan <u>built</u> a practical bicycle in 1839.
    D  Many <u>call</u> him "the inventor of the bicycle."

18. **Which of the following sentences has a linking verb underlined?**

    A  Sara Josephine Baker <u>was</u> a doctor.
    B  She <u>invented</u> a special eyedropper about 100 years ago.
    C  With it, a doctor could <u>put</u> medicine into a newborn baby's eyes.
    D  The medicine <u>prevented</u> one kind of blindness.

19. **Read this sentence.**

    The alarm clock is certainly a helpful invention.

    **Which of these words is an adjective in the sentence?**

    A  clock
    B  is
    C  certainly
    D  helpful

20. **Read this sentence.**

    Levi Hutchins invented the alarm clock but did not patent it.

    **Which word in the sentence is a joining word?**

    A  invented
    B  but
    C  did
    D  not

| Answer Sheet | | | |
|---|---|---|---|
| 16. Ⓐ | Ⓑ | Ⓒ | Ⓓ |
| 17. Ⓐ | Ⓑ | Ⓒ | Ⓓ |
| 18. Ⓐ | Ⓑ | Ⓒ | Ⓓ |
| 19. Ⓐ | Ⓑ | Ⓒ | Ⓓ |
| 20. Ⓐ | Ⓑ | Ⓒ | Ⓓ |

Read each item carefully. Select the best answer. Fill in the circle on the answer sheet below.

1. **Which of the following sentences has _your_ or _you're_ used _incorrectly_?**

   A Your rings are the green ones.
   B You're turn will come soon.
   C Tell me when you're ready.
   D You're the best ring tosser here!

2. **Read this sentence.**

   The kickball field is over ___.

   **Which word would complete the sentence correctly?**

   A they're
   B their
   C there
   D theyre

3. **Which of the following sentences has _its_ or _it's_ used _incorrectly_?**

   A The bowling alley opens it's doors at noon.
   B It's only 11 A.M. now.
   C We like this alley because it's near our homes.
   D Its lanes are clean and smooth, too.

4. **Which of the following sentences uses _a_ and _an_ correctly?**

   A Are you a roller skater or a ice skater?
   B Are you an roller skater or an ice skater?
   C Are you a roller skater or an ice skater?
   D Are you an roller skater or a ice skater?

5. **Read this sentence.**

   Ricki is ___ at checkers than I am.

   **Which choice would complete the sentence correctly?**

   A more good
   B gooder
   C better
   D more better

**Example:**

● Ⓑ Ⓒ Ⓓ

**Answer Sheet**

1. Ⓐ Ⓑ Ⓒ Ⓓ
2. Ⓐ Ⓑ Ⓒ Ⓓ
3. Ⓐ Ⓑ Ⓒ Ⓓ
4. Ⓐ Ⓑ Ⓒ Ⓓ
5. Ⓐ Ⓑ Ⓒ Ⓓ

Read each item carefully. Select the best answer. Fill in the circle on the answer sheet below.

6. Read this sentence.

Tito _____ the bell each time we scored.

Which word would complete the sentence correctly?

A  ringed
B  rang
C  rung
D  ranged

7. Read this sentence.

Our coach has _____ out to the field.

Which word would complete the sentence correctly?

A  went
B  wented
C  goed
D  gone

8. Read each sentence. Look at the underlined word in it. Which sentence is written *incorrectly*?

A  This is a <u>real</u> bowling ball.
B  Al is a <u>real</u> good bowler.
C  Jean is a <u>very</u> good bowler, too.
D  This bowling ball is <u>very</u> heavy!

9. Read this sentence.

I have _____ gymnastics for five years.

Which word would complete the sentence correctly?

A  taked
B  took
C  tooked
D  taken

10. Read this sentence.

My sister _____ a small snack before practice.

Which word would complete the sentence correctly?

A  ate
B  aten
C  eated
D  eaten

**Answer Sheet**

6.  Ⓐ  Ⓑ  Ⓒ  Ⓓ
7.  Ⓐ  Ⓑ  Ⓒ  Ⓓ
8.  Ⓐ  Ⓑ  Ⓒ  Ⓓ
9.  Ⓐ  Ⓑ  Ⓒ  Ⓓ
10. Ⓐ  Ⓑ  Ⓒ  Ⓓ

Name _____

Read each item carefully. Select the best answer. Fill in the circle on the answer sheet below.

11. Which of the following sentences has *your* or *you're* used *incorrectly*?

   A Here is your beanbag.
   B You're the next one in line.
   C Your toss was perfect!
   D Your good at this game!

12. Read this sentence.

   The Birds have scored two runs, but _____ still behind.

   **Which word would complete the sentence correctly?**

   A they're
   B their
   C there
   D theyre

13. Which of the following sentences has *its* or *it's* used *incorrectly*?

   A The skating rink has a sign in its window.
   B The rink opens its doors at 10 A.M.
   C It's only 9:30 A.M. now.
   D Ice skating is not easy, but its fun!

14. Which of the following sentences uses *a* and *an* correctly?

   A I missed a easy shot and made a hard one.
   B I missed an easy shot and made a hard one.
   C I missed an easy shot and made an hard one.
   D I missed a easy shot and made an hard one.

15. Read this sentence.

   Cleve is _____ at tennis than Pat is.

   **Which choice would complete the sentence correctly?**

   A badder
   B worse
   C worser
   D more worse

**Answer Sheet**

11. Ⓐ Ⓑ Ⓒ Ⓓ
12. Ⓐ Ⓑ Ⓒ Ⓓ
13. Ⓐ Ⓑ Ⓒ Ⓓ
14. Ⓐ Ⓑ Ⓒ Ⓓ
15. Ⓐ Ⓑ Ⓒ Ⓓ

Read each item carefully. Select the best answer. Fill in the circle on the answer sheet below.

16. Read this sentence.

    Rachel _____ a volleyball to school yesterday.

    Which word would complete the sentence correctly?

    A  bringed
    B  brang
    C  brung
    D  brought

17. Read this sentence.

    Mario _____ to the school fair last Saturday.

    Which word would complete the sentence correctly?

    A  come
    B  came
    C  comed
    D  camed

18. Read each sentence. Look at the underlined word in it. Which sentence is written *incorrectly*?

    A  This is a <u>real</u> horseshoe.
    B  It is <u>real</u> heavy!
    C  Ina is <u>very</u> good at throwing horseshoes.
    D  She tossed a horseshoe <u>very</u> close to the post.

19. Read this sentence.

    My grandmother _____ us a jigsaw puzzle.

    Which word would complete the sentence correctly?

    A  gived
    B  gave
    C  gaved
    D  given

20. Read this sentence.

    I have _____ many hot dogs at the ballpark.

    Which word would complete the sentence correctly?

    A  ate
    B  aten
    C  eated
    D  eaten

**Answer Sheet**

16. Ⓐ  Ⓑ  Ⓒ  Ⓓ
17. Ⓐ  Ⓑ  Ⓒ  Ⓓ
18. Ⓐ  Ⓑ  Ⓒ  Ⓓ
19. Ⓐ  Ⓑ  Ⓒ  Ⓓ
20. Ⓐ  Ⓑ  Ⓒ  Ⓓ

**Name** _____

# Unit 4 Assessment

 **TEST TIP:** Mark your answers neatly. If you erase, erase completely and cleanly without smudging.

Read each item carefully. Select the best answer. Fill in the circle on the answer sheet below.

1. Read this sentence.

   Andre and I brought our pets with us.

   **Which word in the sentence is a subject pronoun?**

   A  Andre
   B  I
   C  our
   D  us

2. Read this sentence.

   He gave me his puppy to hold.

   **Which word in the sentence is an object pronoun?**

   A  he
   B  me
   C  his
   D  puppy

3. Read each sentence. Look at the underlined word. **Which sentence is written *incorrectly*?**

   A  My brother showed a photo to <u>me</u>.
   B  <u>He</u> took the photo at the zoo.
   C  <u>I</u> did not know what animal it was.
   D  <u>Him</u> said it was an impala.

4. Read each sentence. Look at the underlined word. **Which sentence is *not* correct?**

   A  Carla and <u>I</u> rode ponies.
   B  The ponies were gentle with Carla and <u>me</u>.
   C  Dad gave Carla and <u>I</u> a ride home.
   D  Next time, Carla and <u>I</u> will ride horses.

5. Read this sentence.

   <u>My</u> friend Alan <u>he</u> showed <u>us</u> <u>his</u> six white mice.

   **Which underlined word should be taken out of this sentence?**

   A  my
   B  he
   C  us
   D  his

**Example:**

● Ⓑ Ⓒ Ⓓ

**Answer Sheet**

1. Ⓐ Ⓑ Ⓒ Ⓓ
2. Ⓐ Ⓑ Ⓒ Ⓓ
3. Ⓐ Ⓑ Ⓒ Ⓓ
4. Ⓐ Ⓑ Ⓒ Ⓓ
5. Ⓐ Ⓑ Ⓒ Ⓓ

Read each item carefully. Select the best answer. Fill in the circle on the answer sheet below.

6. Read each sentence. Look at the underlined verb. Which sentence is *not* correct?

    A  Owls <u>hunt</u> at night.
    B  These birds <u>glide</u> silently.
    C  That owl <u>live</u> in a hollow tree.
    D  The owl <u>looks</u> for small animals.

7. Read each sentence. Look at the underlined verb. Which sentence is *not* correct?

    A  The frog in the zoo pond <u>is</u> huge!
    B  That goliath frog <u>are</u> from Africa.
    C  Tree frogs <u>are</u> tiny animals.
    D  Some frogs <u>were</u> in our yard last week.

8. Read each sentence. Which sentence has a past tense verb underlined?

    A  Some people <u>watch</u> birds for fun.
    B  Scientists <u>study</u> birds carefully.
    C  I <u>spotted</u> a hawk this morning.
    D  This book <u>shows</u> photos of several types of hawks.

9. Read each sentence. Which sentence has too many negatives?

    A  The sloth has not moved all day.
    B  It does nothing but hang upside down.
    C  No animal is slower than a sloth.
    D  I would not want no sloth as a pet.

10. Read this sentence.

    The blue whale is the _____ of all mammals.

    Which choice would complete the sentence correctly?

    A  larger
    B  more large
    C  largest
    D  most large

**Answer Sheet**

6.  Ⓐ  Ⓑ  Ⓒ  Ⓓ
7.  Ⓐ  Ⓑ  Ⓒ  Ⓓ
8.  Ⓐ  Ⓑ  Ⓒ  Ⓓ
9.  Ⓐ  Ⓑ  Ⓒ  Ⓓ
10. Ⓐ  Ⓑ  Ⓒ  Ⓓ

Name _____

Read each item carefully. Select the best answer. Fill in the circle on the answer sheet below.

**11.** Read this sentence.

My cousin visited me, and we played with her dog.

Which word in the sentence is a subject pronoun?

A  my
B  me
C  we
D  her

**12.** Read this sentence.

We went to the animal shelter, and my mom chose a cat for us.

Which word in the sentence is an object pronoun?

A  we
B  my
C  mom
D  us

**13.** Read each sentence. Look at the underlined word. Which sentence is written *incorrectly*?

A  <u>I</u> watched an animal program with my aunt.
B  The program was interesting to <u>she</u>.
C  <u>We</u> really liked the baboons.
D  Most of <u>them</u> live in Africa.

**14.** Read each sentence. Look at the underlined word. Which sentence is *not* correct?

A  The ranger showed a snake to Eric and <u>me</u>.
B  Eric and <u>me</u> touched its cool skin.
C  Then Eric and <u>I</u> watched its movements.
D  The ranger taught Eric and <u>me</u> a lot about snakes.

**15.** Read this sentence.

Claire <u>she</u> cares <u>for</u> our dog when <u>we</u> go <u>away</u>.

Which underlined word should be taken out of this sentence?

A  she
B  for
C  we
D  away

**Answer Sheet**

11.  Ⓐ   Ⓑ   Ⓒ   Ⓓ
12.  Ⓐ   Ⓑ   Ⓒ   Ⓓ
13.  Ⓐ   Ⓑ   Ⓒ   Ⓓ
14.  Ⓐ   Ⓑ   Ⓒ   Ⓓ
15.  Ⓐ   Ⓑ   Ⓒ   Ⓓ

Read each item carefully. Select the best answer. Fill in the circle on the answer sheet below.

16. Read each sentence. Look at the underlined verb. Which sentence is *not* correct?

   A  Instead of running, kangaroos <u>hop</u>.
   B  These animals <u>use</u> their strong rear legs.
   C  That kangaroo <u>rests</u> in the shade often.
   D  A hungry kangaroo <u>eat</u> grass and leaves.

17. Read each sentence. Look at the underlined verb. Which sentence is *not* correct?

   A  Foxes <u>are</u> clever hunters.
   B  That fox's home <u>is</u> a den.
   C  Gray foxes <u>is</u> common in the southern states.
   D  Red foxes <u>are</u> common in the northern states.

18. Read each of the sentences. Which sentence has a past tense verb underlined?

   A  Crows usually <u>live</u> in pairs.
   B  One pair <u>visits</u> our yard often.
   C  Last Monday those crows <u>stayed</u> for an hour.
   D  Their loud calls <u>sound</u> harsh.

19. Read each sentence. Which sentence has too many negatives?

   A  The dodo could not fly.
   B  It was not a fast runner.
   C  That big bird had no good way to protect itself.
   D  There aren't no more dodos left on earth.

20. Read this sentence.

   A robin is _____ than a crow.

   Which choice would complete the sentence correctly?

   A  smaller
   B  more small
   C  smallest
   D  most small

**Answer Sheet**

16.  Ⓐ   Ⓑ   Ⓒ   Ⓓ
17.  Ⓐ   Ⓑ   Ⓒ   Ⓓ
18.  Ⓐ   Ⓑ   Ⓒ   Ⓓ
19.  Ⓐ   Ⓑ   Ⓒ   Ⓓ
20.  Ⓐ   Ⓑ   Ⓒ   Ⓓ

Name _____

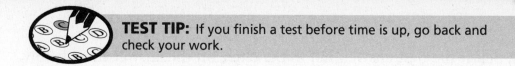

**TEST TIP:** If you finish a test before time is up, go back and check your work.

Read each item carefully. Select the best answer. Fill in the circle on the answer sheet below.

1. **Read this sentence.**

   Which mountains have you climbed.

   **How should the sentence be changed to make it correct?**

   A Change the period to an exclamation point.
   B Change the period to a question mark.
   C Make the first letter in **mountains** a capital letter.
   D Make no change. It is correct as written.

2. **Read this sentence.**

   Our <u>class</u> read a <u>legend</u> about two <u>mountains</u> in <u>mexico</u>.

   **Which underlined word should be capitalized?**

   A class
   B legend
   C mountains
   D mexico

3. **Read this sentence.**

   Did <u>Doctor</u> Lynch examine the mountain climber?

   **How could the underlined word be written as an abbreviation?**

   A Doc.
   B doc.
   C Dr.
   D Dr

4. **Read each sentence. Which sentence has the book title in it written correctly?**

   A I am reading "Rafting on the Snake River."
   B Last week I finished <u>A bridge across the Mississippi</u>.
   C Next I will read <u>The Great Plains Today</u>.
   D I also want to read "Texas hill country tales."

5. **Read this sentence.**

   <u>The rocks of this canyon</u> are colorful.

   **How could the underlined words be written as a possessive expression?**

   A this canyon's rocks
   B this canyons' rocks
   C this canyon' rocks
   D this canyons rocks

**Example:**

● Ⓑ Ⓒ Ⓓ

**Answer Sheet**

1. Ⓐ Ⓑ Ⓒ Ⓓ
2. Ⓐ Ⓑ Ⓒ Ⓓ
3. Ⓐ Ⓑ Ⓒ Ⓓ
4. Ⓐ Ⓑ Ⓒ Ⓓ
5. Ⓐ Ⓑ Ⓒ Ⓓ

Read each item carefully. Select the best answer. Fill in the circle on the answer sheet below.

6. **Read this sentence.**

   <u>We have</u> collected rocks in the Nevada desert.

   **How could the underlined words be written as a contraction?**

   A  weve
   B  we'eve
   C  wev'e
   D  we've

7. **Read each sentence. Look at the commas. Which sentence is written correctly?**

   A  This park has creeks, caves and, waterfalls.
   B  Campers, hikers, and swimmers, enjoy it.
   C  The best months to visit are June, July, and August.
   D  The park is wet, cold, and, dark in winter.

8. **Read this sentence.**

   No you cannot drink the water from the Great Salt Lake.

   **Where should a comma be placed in this sentence?**

   A  after **no**
   B  after **drink**
   C  after **water**
   D  after **Great**

9. **Read each sentence. Which sentence needs to have quotation marks added to it?**

   A  The guide told us to watch out for flash floods.
   B  She said that rain was falling in the area.
   C  A dry canyon can suddenly fill with water, she said.
   D  She said to stay on high ground.

10. **Read each sentence. Look at the direct quotation. Which sentence uses punctuation marks correctly?**

    A  "Can you name all five Great Lakes? asked Mitch.
    B  "Yes, I have an easy way to remember them," said Tara.
    C  "Their initials make the word *homes,* she continued."
    D  "The Great Lakes are Huron, Ontario, Michigan, Erie, and Superior." she said.

**Answer Sheet**

6.  Ⓐ  Ⓑ  Ⓒ  Ⓓ
7.  Ⓐ  Ⓑ  Ⓒ  Ⓓ
8.  Ⓐ  Ⓑ  Ⓒ  Ⓓ
9.  Ⓐ  Ⓑ  Ⓒ  Ⓓ
10. Ⓐ  Ⓑ  Ⓒ  Ⓓ

Read each item carefully. Select the best answer. Fill in the circle on the answer sheet below.

11. Read this sentence.

    what a huge cave this is!

    **How should the sentence be changed to make it correct?**

    A Change the exclamation point to a period.

    B Change the exclamation point to a question mark.

    C Make the first letter in **what** a capital letter.

    D Make no change. It is correct as written.

12. Read this sentence.

    My <u>cousins</u> visited the largest <u>cave</u> in <u>kentucky</u> last <u>year</u>.

    **Which underlined word should be capitalized?**

    A cousins

    B cave

    C kentucky

    D year

13. Read this sentence.

    My teacher, <u>Mister</u> Parsons, is the soccer coach.

    **How could the underlined word be written as an abbreviation?**

    A Mr.

    B M.r.

    C MR.

    D mr.

14. Read each sentence. Which sentence has the book title in it written correctly?

    A I am reading <u>Hiking in Alaska</u>.

    B Last week I finished <u>Trails for young hikers</u>.

    C Next week I will read "Everglades Forever."

    D I also want to read "Tales of desert journeys."

15. Read this sentence.

    The <u>leaves of the trees</u> are red and gold.

    **How could the underlined words be written as a possessive expression?**

    A the tree's leaves

    B the trees's leaves

    C the trees' leaves

    D the trees leaves

**Answer Sheet**

11. Ⓐ Ⓑ Ⓒ Ⓓ
12. Ⓐ Ⓑ Ⓒ Ⓓ
13. Ⓐ Ⓑ Ⓒ Ⓓ
14. Ⓐ Ⓑ Ⓒ Ⓓ
15. Ⓐ Ⓑ Ⓒ Ⓓ

Read each item carefully. Select the best answer. Fill in the circle on the answer sheet below.

16. Read this sentence.

    Those streams <u>are not</u> easy to cross.

    How could the underlined words be written as a contraction?

    A  are'nt
    B  aren't
    C  arent
    D  arn't

17. Read each sentence. Look at the commas. Which sentence is written correctly?

    A  Moose, deer, and elk roam these wild lands.
    B  They wander near, lakes, ponds and creeks.
    C  That bear looks large, strong, and, hungry.
    D  Do not tease, chase, or scare, that skunk!

18. Read this sentence.

    Yes a hurricane brings heavy rains and strong winds.

    Where should a comma be placed in this sentence?

    A  after yes
    B  after hurricane
    C  after brings
    D  after rains

19. Read each sentence. Which sentence needs to have quotation marks added to it?

    A  My friend told me about a nature show on TV.
    B  You'll really like it, he said.
    C  He explained that it was filmed in Australia.
    D  He said he would find out when it will be shown again.

20. Read each sentence. Look at the direct quotation. Which sentence uses punctuation marks correctly?

    A  Have you hiked on a volcano? "asked Jared."
    B  "Yes, I have hiked on Mount Hood, said Ellen.
    C  "Was it scary?" asked Jared.
    D  "I did not expect it to erupt" Ellen replied.

**Answer Sheet**

16. Ⓐ  Ⓑ  Ⓒ  Ⓓ
17. Ⓐ  Ⓑ  Ⓒ  Ⓓ
18. Ⓐ  Ⓑ  Ⓒ  Ⓓ
19. Ⓐ  Ⓑ  Ⓒ  Ⓓ
20. Ⓐ  Ⓑ  Ⓒ  Ⓓ

**Lesson 1** Read the following sentences. Write *S* next to the sentences that are complete.

1. Went on a field trip to a natural history museum. ____

2. Our teacher asked us to stay with the group. ____

3. We all stared at the dinosaur bones. ____

4. We saw many fossils. ____

5. A movie in the museum theater. ____

6. It showed pictures of dinosaurs. ____

7. Looked very scary! ____

8. Some students in our class. ____

9. Asked the guide many questions. ____

10. I hope we get to visit again soon. ____

**Lesson 2** Underline the subject in each sentence.

1. The morning was clear and bright.

2. My uncle took me to the mountains.

3. He parked the truck on the side of the road.

4. A wide path led into the hills.

5. We hiked up the path into the forest.

6. The pine trees towered above our heads.

7. Sunlight spotted the path.

8. My uncle pointed to a field.

9. A mother deer drank from a stream.

10. Two young deer played in the tall grass.

**Name** _____ 159

**Lesson 3** Underline the predicate in each sentence.

1. The storm started suddenly.

2. The blue sky turned dark.

3. Big waves rocked the ship.

4. The wild wind tore its sails.

5. Rainwater soaked the deck.

6. The crew gripped the sides.

7. The captain steered toward the shore.

8. Sunlight broke through the clouds.

9. The crew cheered.

10. The ship survived the storm.

**Lesson 4** Write *T* next to each telling sentence and *A* next to each asking sentence.

1. What is your favorite subject in school? _____

2. My favorite subject is science. _____

3. What do you like about science class? _____

4. I learn about the world around me. _____

5. What have you studied this year? _____

6. Have you gone on any field trips? _____

7. This year we are studying ocean animals. _____

8. Our class went on a field trip to the ocean. _____

9. We saw a young dolphin. _____

10. It swam beside its mother. _____

**Lesson 5** Write a period to end each command and an exclamation point to end each exclamation.

1. Yippee, we're baking a cake today____

2. Measure three cups of flour____

3. Oh no, I spilled some____

4. Mix in the sugar____

5. Break two eggs into the bowl____

6. I can't wait to taste it____

7. Put it in the oven carefully____

8. Take the cake out after 30 minutes____

9. It's finally done____

10. Mmm, this is delicious____

**Lesson 6** Circle the verb in each sentence. Then underline the prepositional phrase that tells more about the verb.

1. My cat Buster ran down the stairs.

2. My mother pointed to a tiny animal.

3. A mouse scampered toward the kitchen.

4. Buster sneaked under the table.

5. A chair fell onto the floor.

6. The noise rang through the air.

7. The mouse froze near the sink.

8. Buster jumped at the mouse.

9. The mouse ran into his hole.

10. Buster meowed at the hole.

Name _____

**Lesson 7** Write *X* next to each sentence fragment.

1. We are studying our town's history. _____

2. My favorite subject. _____

3. Settled here many years ago. _____

4. Native Americans once lived here. _____

5. My friend Shawna. _____

6. We read a book about pioneers. _____

7. A long, difficult journey. _____

8. Made a fort out of toothpicks. _____

**Lesson 8** Write *X* next to the sentence that gives more information.

1. **a.** Summer vacation was fun. _____

   **b.** Last summer we visited my grandparents in Hawaii. _____

2. **a.** We stayed with my grandparents in their small, pink beach house. _____

   **b.** We stayed at their house. _____

3. **a.** From my window I could see miles of white sand and blue ocean. _____

   **b.** My view was pretty good. _____

4. **a.** I went snorkeling in a beautiful bay and saw fish with colorful scales. _____

   **b.** I had fun snorkeling. _____

5. **a.** My brother got sunburned. _____

   **b.** My brother fell asleep in the sun and ended up with a painful sunburn. _____

6. **a.** We went on a hike. _____

   **b.** We hiked for hours through the lush green rainforest. _____

7. **a.** We went to a luau where we ate roast pork and steamed vegetables. _____

   **b.** The food at the luau was good. _____

8. **a.** I enjoyed our vacation. _____

   **b.** I enjoyed hiking through the countryside and seeing my grandparents. _____

Name _____

**Lesson 9** Underline the six compound sentences in the paragraphs below. Circle the joining words.

The Grand Canyon is an amazing place. The canyon is almost 300 miles long, and it is as much as a mile deep in places. You can see for miles from the rim of the canyon. The canyon walls look like they've been painted different colors, but they're actually made up of many layers of rock. Each layer was laid down at a different time in the earth's history. The oldest rocks in the canyon may be two billion years old!

Visitors to the Grand Canyon can go to the North Rim, or they can visit the South Rim. Both areas offer beautiful views. Many tourists hike down to the bottom of the canyon, but others ride mules down instead. The Colorado River flows through the canyon, and you can raft down the river with a guide. Grand Canyon National Park is a truly amazing place, and it's well worth a visit.

**Lesson 10** Write *X* after each run-on sentence. On a separate sheet of paper rewrite each run-on sentence correctly. Add a comma and a linking word.

1. My sister and I are twins I was born first. _____

2. My mother used to dress us the same, but now we dress differently. _____

3. My sister likes soccer I like tennis. _____

4. My sister has long braids, but I have short hair. _____

5. Teachers confuse us sometimes, but our parents can tell us apart. _____

6. I want to be an astronaut my sister wants to be an actress. _____

7. My sister was in the school play she had the lead role. _____

8. She remembered all of her lines, but some other actors missed their cues. _____

9. My parents and I sat in the front row, and we could see all the action. _____

10. My sister did a terrific job I am proud of her. _____

Name _____

**Lesson 11** Circle the underlined noun in each sentence. Next to each sentence, write *person, place,* or *thing* to tell what the noun names.

1. The park was crowded. _____

2. The wind blew steadily. _____

3. The day was clear and sunny. _____

4. We flew our kites for hours. _____

5. My kite looks like a fish. _____

6. One kite got caught in a tree. _____

7. The kite's owner climbed the tree. _____

8. He passed the kite to his friend. _____

9. Its string was tangled around a branch. _____

10. We helped him tie new string onto the kite. _____

**Lesson 12** Read the sentences. Decide which underlined word or phrase in each sentence is a proper noun. Circle it.

1. Ruth Handler was an inventor.

2. She was born in Denver.

3. That city is the capital of Colorado.

4. She was married to a man named Elliot Handler.

5. Together they moved to California.

6. They helped start a company called Mattel.

7. Ruth Handler invented a doll named Barbie.

8. She named it after her daughter, Barbara.

9. Ruth and Elliot Handler also had a son named Kenneth.

10. They created a doll named Ken, too.

**Lesson 13** Underline the word in bold type that is a plural noun. Circle the letter that was added to form each plural.

1. Giraffes are the tallest **animals** on **Earth**.

2. They **have** very long **necks**.

3. **Giraffes** reach up into treetops for **food**.

4. They **live** in grassy **areas** in Africa.

5. A giraffe's **coat** has brown and yellow **markings**.

6. The **giraffe** has two **horns** on its head.

7. It can close its **nostrils** to keep out **sand**.

8. A giraffe usually **sleeps** standing on its **legs**.

**Lesson 14** Choose a pronoun from the word bank that can take the place of the underlined word or phrase. Write the pronoun on the line.

| he | she | him | us | her | we | them | they |
|----|-----|-----|----|----|----|------|------|

1. <u>Chita Rivera</u> is an actress and dancer. _____

2. <u>Chita's father</u> was born in Puerto Rico. _____

3. <u>Mr. Rivera</u> died when Chita was seven. _____

4. <u>Chita</u> had talent. _____

5. Chita took <u>ballet lessons</u> when she was young. _____

6. <u>Doris Jones</u> was Chita's dance teacher. _____

7. Doris taught <u>Chita</u> a lot. _____

8. Chita stayed with <u>her uncle</u> in New York while she went to dancing school. _____

9. <u>Audiences</u> love Chita. _____

10. <u>You and I</u> could go to one of Chita's shows. _____

Name _____

**Lesson 15** Choose a pronoun from the word bank that can take the place of each phrase. Write the pronoun on the line.

| This | That | These | Those |
|------|------|-------|-------|

1. <u>The store we are in</u> is my favorite pet store. _____

2. <u>The bag I am holding</u> is full of puppy food. _____

3. <u>The bags on the shelf</u> hold cat food. _____

4. <u>The building across the street</u> is a kennel. _____

5. <u>The bones I am holding</u> are treats for the dogs. _____

6. <u>The biscuits in my pocket</u> are good for puppies. _____

7. <u>The book on the shelf</u> is about dog training. _____

8. <u>The book in my hand</u> is about poodles. _____

9. <u>The big pillows in the corner</u> are dog beds. _____

10. <u>The leather ring in my hand</u> is a dog collar. _____

**Lesson 16** Circle the underlined word in each sentence that is an action verb.

1. The <u>crowd</u> <u>yelled</u> loudly.

2. Soon the <u>players</u> <u>ran</u> onto the court.

3. The <u>fans</u> <u>cheered</u> wildly.

4. The referee <u>blew</u> her <u>whistle</u>.

5. <u>The</u> other referee <u>tossed</u> the ball <u>into</u> the air.

6. A player <u>dribbled</u> the <u>ball</u> down the court.

7. She <u>shot</u> the ball <u>toward</u> the hoop.

8. The ball <u>bounced</u> off <u>the</u> rim.

9. Her teammate <u>caught</u> the <u>ball</u>.

10. She <u>tossed</u> it into the <u>basket</u>!

**Name** _____

**Lesson 17** Circle the verb in ( ) that tells about action that happened in the past. Write the verb on the line.

1. Last night an opossum _____ across our yard. (race/raced)

2. It _____ through a hole in the fence. (climbed/climb)

3. Hans and I _____ for the opossum. (looking/looked)

4. We _____ everywhere. (search/searched)

5. The opossum _____ food last night. (wanted/wants)

6. It _____ for food in our yard. (look/looked)

7. This morning we _____ the fence. (fix/fixed)

8. Last week I _____ another opossum. (watched/watch)

9. Six babies _____ onto her back! (clutching/clutched)

10. Their pink tails _____ behind them. (trail/trailed)

**Lesson 18** Circle the verb in ( ) that fits in each sentence. Write the verb on the line to complete each sentence.

1. Giant clams _____ rare. (is/are)

2. That clam's shell _____ two feet wide. (is/are)

3. The soft clam _____ inside the shell. (is/are)

4. Yesterday two divers _____ on the ocean floor. (was/were)

5. They _____ close to a giant clam. (was/were)

6. One diver _____ curious. (was/were)

7. The other diver _____ afraid of the clam. (was/were)

8. Giant clams _____ dangerous. (is/are)

9. The clam's muscle _____ very strong. (is/are)

10. The divers _____ careful. (was/were)

Name _____

**Lesson 19** Circle the adjective that describes each underlined noun.

1. Some students in Virginia built a huge <u>airplane</u> out of paper.

2. They worked with local <u>scientists</u> to build a fast <u>airplane</u> that could fly far.

3. The students tried different <u>shapes</u>.

4. Finally they chose the graceful <u>shape</u> of a pelican.

5. They used white <u>paper</u>, glue, and tape to build the plane.

6. The huge <u>wings</u> measured 30 feet, 6 inches long.

7. The scientists helped the students send the airplane on its first <u>flight</u>.

8. It flew 114 feet, 9 inches as the hopeful <u>students</u> watched.

9. The white pelican set a new <u>record</u> for paper airplane flight.

**Lesson 20** Choose a word from the word bank that belongs in each sentence. Write that word in the blank.

| and | but | or |
|---|---|---|

1. Adobe bricks are made from mud _____ water mixed together.

2. Either straw _____ hay is added to the mix.

3. The mix is stirred _____ then shaped into bricks.

4. Adobe bricks must be dried for weeks, _____ else they will fall apart.

5. The dried bricks are used to build both houses _____ walls.

6. A mud paint made from soil _____ water covers the adobe bricks.

7. This paint can be put on by hand _____ with a tool called a spade.

8. Adobe homes are beautiful, _____ they need a lot of care.

9. Rain _____ wind will damage the mud walls over time.

10. Long ago many people knew how to build adobe homes, _____ today only a few builders know this skill.

**Lesson 21** Write *your* or *you're* in each blank. Remember to begin each sentence with a capital letter.

1. _____ hat is quite fancy.

2. _____ going to be a hit at the costume party.

3. If _____ wearing a hat, I'm going to wear one, too.

4. _____ costume won a prize last year.

5. Did you say _____ going to wear that mask?

6. _____ going to scare everyone!

7. Can we go to the party in _____ car?

8. Please ask _____ dad if he will drive us.

9. I think _____ going to win a prize.

10. _____ going to have to make a speech, too.

**Lesson 22** Circle the word in ( ) that completes each sentence correctly.

1. Look at the dancers over (there/their)!

2. (There/They're) so strong and graceful!

3. That small dancer over (their/there) is very talented.

4. (They're/There) all good dancers.

5. (There/Their) costumes are very unusual.

6. (They're/Their) company was started in 1958.

7. (Their/There) company's founder, Alvin Ailey, was a famous dancer.

8. (Their/They're) very popular in Europe and in the United States.

9. (There/Their) dances have been shown on television.

10. Tonight (there/they're) performing to jazz music.

Name _____

**Lesson 23** Write *its* or *it's* to complete each sentence. Remember to begin each sentence with a capital letter.

1. This turtle makes _____ home in South America.

2. _____ a very unusual creature.

3. _____ name is *mata-mata,* which means "loose skin."

4. _____ head, legs, and arms are covered in loose skin.

5. _____ mouth can open very wide.

6. _____ like a trap door.

7. _____ main food is small fish.

8. Sometimes _____ covered with green algae.

9. Then _____ almost impossible to see.

10. _____ easy to mistake a mata-mata for a leaf.

**Lesson 24** Write *a* or *an* to complete each sentence.

1. Matt wanted to do _____ art project.

2. First he bought _____ set of paints.

3. Then he put on _____old shirt.

4. "I'll paint _____ picture of my house," he said.

5. He spent _____ hour mixing the paints.

6. He mixed _____ bright red color for the front door.

7. He decided to put _____ lot of unusual things in his painting.

8. He painted _____ elephant in the front yard.

9. He painted _____ airplane in the driveway.

10. "What _____ imagination!" his mom said.

**Name** _____

**Lesson 25** Circle the word in ( ) that belongs in each sentence.

1. The judges thought the dog show was (better/gooder) than the cat show.

2. The spaniels looked good as they pranced around the ring, but the poodles looked even (better/more good).

3. Mimi is a (better/more better) dog show contestant than Fifi.

4. Mimi usually jumps too far, but Fifi is a (worser/worse) jumper than Mimi.

5. The judges liked the dogs' tricks, but they liked their fashions (better/gooder).

6. Fifi looked good in her fuzzy yellow coat, but Mimi looked (more better/better) in her blue one.

7. The terriers' haircuts were good, but the poodles' cuts were (better/more good).

8. The poodles' yapping was (more bad/worse) than the terriers' barking.

9. The beagles looked silly in sweaters, but the hounds looked even (badder/worse).

10. This year's show was (better/more good) than last year's show.

**Lesson 26** Circle the word that completes each sentence.

1. We (sung/sang) "Happy Birthday" to my dad.

2. When the telephone (ringed/rang), we stopped singing.

3. My dad's brother (sang/singed) "Happy Birthday" over the phone.

4. When the doorbell (rang/ringed), we dragged my dad to the door.

5. A clown had (brung/brought) a bunch of balloons.

6. The clown (sing/sang) a silly song.

7. We (brought/brang) the clown inside.

8. The clown (ringed/rang) a bell after Dad opened each gift.

9. Before long the clown had (sang/sung) all the songs he knew.

10. I wish we had (bringed/brought) two clowns.

Name _____

**Extra Practice**

**Lesson 27** Underline the word in ( ) that completes each sentence correctly.

1. On Monday a white cat (came/come) to our door during dinner.

2. I didn't know where it had (come/came) from.

3. On Tuesday a little spotted cat (came/come), too.

4. I (gone/went) onto the porch.

5. The spotted cat (come/came) right up to me.

6. The white cat had (went/gone) away.

7. The cats didn't (came/come) back until Friday.

8. I wondered where they had (went/gone).

9. I (gone/went) all over the neighborhood looking for them.

10. They had (gone/go) to a different house every night!

**Lesson 28** Write *very* or *real* to complete each sentence correctly.

1. The movie showed ten oarsmen rowing _____ hard.

2. The work seemed _____ difficult.

3. In _____ life, the boat was in a small pool of water.

4. The oarsmen were _____ strong.

5. Was that a _____ octopus?

6. It looked _____ scary on the screen.

7. It was actually _____ small.

8. The crew took pictures of a _____ octopus.

9. They used special equipment to make the octopus look _____ big.

10. I hope I never see a _____ octopus that big!

**Lesson 29** Circle the word in ( ) that belongs in each sentence.

1. My family (taken/took) a trip to Chicago.

2. Dad (give/gave) me a camera of my own.

3. I have (taken/took) many pictures with it.

4. I (took/taken) some pictures of Lake Michigan.

5. Dad has (gived/given) me good advice.

6. Never (took/take) a picture with your eyes closed.

7. (Give/Given) yourself time to find the best shot.

8. I (taked/took) one great picture of a sailboat.

9. I (gave/given) that picture to Dad.

10. He has (gived/given) me some fine pictures, too.

**Lesson 30** Circle the word in ( ) that belongs in each sentence.

1. I (sleeped/slept) poorly last night.

2. Maybe I had (aten/eaten) too much.

3. I (ate/eated) two hot dogs at the ball game.

4. I usually (eat/eaten) just one.

5. I also (ate/eaten) some chili before bed.

6. I wish I had (eaten/ate) less!

7. I usually (slept/sleep) like a rock.

8. My dog (slept/sleeped) poorly, too.

9. He also had (eaten/aten) too much.

10. He (eated/ate) three dishes of food!

Name _____

**Lesson 31** Write a subject pronoun from the word bank that can take the place of the underlined word or phrase. You will use some pronouns more than once.

| They | She | It | He | I | We |
|------|-----|-----|-----|-----|-----|

1. Dolphins are related to whales. _____

2. The killer whale is the largest member of the dolphin family. _____

3. Fish and squid are dolphins' main food. _____

4. Baby dolphins are born in the water. _____

5. A mother dolphin cares for her baby for about a year. _____

6. Shirley works at a marine mammal center. _____

7. Leo helps her care for dolphins there. _____

8. You and I can visit the center next Saturday. _____

**Lesson 32** Write an object pronoun from the word bank that can take the place of the words in ( ). You will use some pronouns more than once.

| him | her | us | them | me | it |
|-----|-----|-----|------|-----|-----|

1. Connie went with _____ to the zoo. (Bob)

2. The visit was fun for _____. (Connie)

3. Both of _____ went to the hippo pond. (Connie and Bob)

4. Connie and Bob saw _____ in the water. (three pygmy hippos)

5. A zookeeper told _____ about the hippos. (Bob)

6. "The zoo brought _____ here from Liberia," he said. (the hippos)

7. Then the zookeeper spoke to _____. (Connie)

8. "The hippos will swim to _____ at feeding time," the zookeeper said. (the zookeeper)

**Lesson 33** Choose a pronoun from the word bank to replace each phrase in ( ). Write it on the line. Use a capital letter if it is the first word in the sentence.

| I | she | they | he | we | us | him | them | her |
|---|-----|------|----|----|----|-----|------|-----|

1. _____ went for a hike in the desert. (Hannah's family and I)

2. _____ saw a rattlesnake on a rock. (Hannah)

3. A cat followed _____ to our campground. (Hannah and me)

4. _____ heard a coyote barking. (Hannah's father)

5. A ranger told _____ about an interesting hike. (Hannah)

6. He also warned _____ about the desert sun. (Hannah and me)

7. _____ saw an owl's nest in a cactus. (Hannah's mother)

8. A blue jay stole a cracker from _____. (Hannah's brother)

9. The guide drove _____ to a cool, clear spring. (Hannah's family and me)

10. _____ drank some water there. (Hannah's father and mother)

**Lesson 34** Underline the phrase in ( ) that fits each sentence.

1. (Elena and I/Elena and me) looked for owls one night last week.

2. Aunt Ida led (me and Elena/Elena and me) through the forest.

3. She showed (Elena and me/Elena and I) an old crow's nest.

4. (I and Elena/Elena and I) saw a great horned owl in the nest.

5. The owl stared at (Elena and I/Elena and me) and called out *hoo-hoo.*

6. Then it flew past (Elena and me/me and Elena) in search of food.

7. Aunt Ida brought (Elena and I/Elena and me) back to the cabin at midnight.

8. She gave (me and Elena/Elena and me) a book about owls the next day.

9. (Elena and I/I and Elena) read about great horned owls.

10. (Me and Elena/Elena and I) will bring a camera on our next hike.

Name _____

**Lesson 35** Read each sentence. Draw a line through any subject pronoun that does not belong.

1. This new video game it is called "Jungle Maze."

2. Al and I both like it a lot.

3. Two baby elephants they are separated from their mother.

4. The jungle it is filled with danger.

5. The boy elephant is very thirsty, and he is hungry, too.

6. He must watch out for crocodiles near the river.

7. His older sister she is being chased by lions.

8. They are good hunters, but she is very brave.

9. The mother elephant she looks for her babies.

10. The explorers they must guide the young elephants to her.

**Lesson 36** Circle the verb in ( ) that fits in each sentence.

1. Koalas (come/comes) from Australia.

2. They (spends/spend) most of their time in the branches of eucalyptus trees.

3. A wild koala (does/do) not drink any water.

4. It (get/gets) water by eating leaves.

5. The name *koala* (comes/come) from an Australian word meaning "no drink."

6. Many people in Australia (uses/use) other names for the koala, such as *bangaroo*.

7. Koalas (looks/look) cuddly and soft.

8. But their sharp, curved claws (make/makes) them dangerous to hold.

9. Most koalas (sleeps/sleep) in the trees during the day.

10. A baby koala (stays/stay) in its mother's pouch for at least six months.

**Lesson 37** Write *S* next to each sentence with a singular subject. Write *P* next to each sentence with a plural subject. Circle the word in ( ) that fits in each sentence.

1. Mauritius (is/are) an island in the Indian Ocean. ___

2. This island (was/were) the home of the dodo bird. ___

3. Dodos (was/were) about the size of turkeys. ___

4. Their wings (were/was) so short that they could not fly. ___

5. The dodo's beak (was/were) very large. ___

6. Its feathers (were/was) curly. ___

7. Pigeons (is/are) distant relatives of the dodo. ___

8. The dodo bird (is/are) now extinct. ___

9. Dodos (were/was) hunted for food in the 1500s. ___

10. The dodos (were/are) all dead by 1681. ___

**Lesson 38** Rewrite each sentence so it tells about the past. Use another sheet of paper. Be sure to change the form of the verb in bold type.

1. In the spring, I **visit** California with my family.

2. We **watch** for whales through a telescope.

3. The whales **pass** by on their way to Alaska.

4. My sister **counts** the whales.

5. They **travel** in pods, or groups.

6. Some people **follow** the whales in boats.

7. The whales **spout** water into the air.

8. The tourists **cheer** at the sight.

9. My mother **paints** pictures of marine mammals.

10. She **listens** to the songs of humpback whales.

**Name** _____

**Lesson 39** Underline each negative in the sentences below. Write *X* next to each sentence that has too many negatives. Rewrite these sentences correctly on a separate sheet of paper.

1. We had not seen our pet turtle Tiny for days. ____

2. Tiny was not sitting on his favorite rock no more. ____

3. He was not in none of his favorite hiding places. ____

4. I thought we might never see Tiny again. ____

5. Tiny did not leave no clues behind. ____

6. We didn't remember one important fact. ____

7. Turtles don't like cold weather. ____

8. We hadn't had no sunshine for days! ____

9. We were not looking for Tiny in the right places. ____

10. I couldn't believe it when I found Tiny under my bed! ____

**Lesson 40** Underline the word or phrase in ( ) that fits in each sentence.

1. Are llamas the (most tall/tallest) animals in South America?

2. Giraffes are (more tall/taller) than elephants.

3. Is a dog's bark (louder/more loud) than a wolf's howl?

4. Have you ever seen an insect (smaller/more small) than an ant?

5. Cheetahs are the (fastest/more fast) of all land animals.

6. Is a hippo (more big/bigger) than a rhino?

7. Does a rabbit have the (softer/softest) fur of any animal?

8. Crows are the (smarter/smartest) birds of all, according to my grandmother.

9. Wild turkeys are (smarter/smartest) than barnyard turkeys.

10. The California condor has the (longer/longest) wings of any bird in North America.

**Lesson 41** Underline the mistake in each sentence. Rewrite the sentence correctly.

1. the sky is cloudy today. _____

2. Do you think it will rain! _____

3. Did you see the lightning. _____

4. Here comes the thunder? _____

5. Wow, that thunder is loud. _____

6. get your raincoat. _____

7. Don't step in that puddle _____

8. Hurrah, the plants are getting the water they need _____

_____

9. i like walking in the rain. _____

10. when will this storm end? _____

**Lesson 42** Circle the words in bold type that need to begin with a capital letter.

1. A few **years** ago I went on a trip to **kansas**.

2. I **wanted** to visit **tallgrass prairie national preserve**.

3. To get there I drove toward **strong city** on the **highway**.

4. I stopped at a **guest ranch** in the **flint hills**.

5. My friend **donte** was already there at the **bunkhouse**.

6. The next morning **we** walked through the hills near **fox creek**.

7. After that we drove to a **region** called **konza prairie**.

8. We saw **grasses** six feet tall, and we also walked along **king's creek**.

9. I then left my **friend** and drove to **kansas state university**.

10. **professor lloyd c. hulburt** of that **university** helped protect Konza Prairie from development.

**Lesson 43** Circle the abbreviation or initial in ( ) that can take the place of the underlined word.

1. <u>Mister</u> Oliner went for a ride on his bicycle. (mr./Mr.)

2. He wanted to visit the top of <u>Mount</u> Cielo. (Mt./Mat.)

3. For the first few miles he rode uphill on Keller <u>Street</u>. (st./St.)

4. Along the way he met <u>Doctor</u> Westmoreland. (Dr./DR)

5. She had been riding her bicycle in <u>North</u> Lake Park. (n./N.)

6. Together they rode for ten miles along Redwood <u>Road</u>. (Rd./rd.)

7. Then they turned left at Skyline <u>Avenue</u>. (Ave./ave.)

8. About an hour later, they reached John <u>Paul</u> Stoopa Park. (p./P.)

9. It started to rain, so they turned onto Ames <u>Drive</u> and rode home. (dr./Dr.)

10. They decided to meet the next weekend to ride in <u>José</u> Suarez Park. (J./j.)

**Lesson 44** Underline each book title. Then make this proofreading mark (⹀) under the letters in each title that should be capitalized.

1. Joanie read a book about amusement parks called exciting rides of the world.

2. At the library, she found a book titled theme parks on parade.

3. Another book was called rides of a lifetime.

4. Joanie looked at a book about roller coasters titled rocket mountain.

5. At the book store, Joanie found a book with the title red hot roller coasters.

6. She also found a book called a trip to tivoli gardens.

7. A book about rides in New York was titled the coney island boardwalk.

8. A book about Florida amusement parks was called fun in florida.

9. California's parks were described in a book called kingdoms of magic.

10. Joanie finally decided to buy a book called roller coasters forever.

**Lesson 45** Circle the word in ( ) that belongs in each sentence.

1. A (satellite's/satellites) orbit is the path it takes around a planet.

2. A (satellite's/satellites') shape and size depend on the job it does.

3. Some satellites follow (storms'/storm's) paths.

4. Others keep track of (airplane's/airplanes') locations.

5. Some satellites have taken pictures of a (planets/planet's) clouds.

6. Some satellites record our (sun's/suns') activity.

7. To reach outer space, rockets must overcome (gravity's/gravitys) force.

8. (Russia's/Russias') Yuri Gagarin was the first person to travel in space.

9. (Americas'/America's) *Apollo 11* spacecraft was the first to take people to the moon.

10. (Florida's/Floridas') space center has a launching pad for space shuttles.

**Lesson 46** Rewrite the words in ( ) as contractions.

1. (I am) planning a trip to the rainforest in Nicaragua with my sister. _____

2. (We have) wanted to visit the rainforest for a long time. _____

3. We (have not) bought our airplane tickets yet. _____

4. (We have) already gathered maps, a tent, and water bottles. _____

5. Sarita wants to go because (she is) interested in tropical plants. _____

6. (I have) become interested in the animals of the rainforest. _____

7. (We will) hike for a week. _____

8. Do you think (it is) easy to hike in rainforests? _____

9. (They are) full of insects and snakes. _____

10. (We will) wear sturdy boots. _____

Name _____

**Lesson 47** Write *C* next to each sentence that uses commas correctly. Add missing commas to the other sentences.

1. All plants, animals, and human beings need water to survive. _____

2. Water is found naturally as a solid, a liquid, and a gas. _____

3. Liquid water is found in rain, rivers lakes, and oceans. _____

4. Water is used for drinking cleaning and cooking. _____

5. Water is also used to make paper steel, and soft drinks. _____

6. Swimming sailing surfing, and fishing are popular water sports. _____

7. Water falls from the sky in the form of rain hail, snow, sleet, and fog. _____

8. Over time water can carve cliffs valleys, and canyons. _____

9. The three highest waterfalls are in Venezuela Switzerland and California. _____

10. Skiers snowboarders and ice skaters all use forms of frozen water. _____

**Lesson 48** Add a comma to each answer.

1. Does the ocean rise and fall? Yes the rise and fall of the ocean is called the tide.

2. Is the water highest when the tide is out? No it is highest when the tide is in.

3. Does the moon change the tide? Yes the pull of the moon changes the tide.

4. Does the tide rise and fall every day? Yes the tide rises and falls twice each day.

5. Do tides exist only in the ocean? No there are tides in every body of water.

6. Do tides help people? Yes tides help keep some boat channels deep.

7. Are tidal waves caused by changes in tides? No they're caused by earthquakes.

8. Do tides affect beaches? Yes at high tide, more of a beach is covered with water.

9. Can plants and animals live on the seashore? Yes they live in this tidal zone.

10. Can you see creatures in a tidepool? Yes you can see starfish, sea anemones, and crabs.

**Lesson 49** Add quotation marks to the sentences that need them. Circle each sentence that is already correct.

1. "Have you ever been to Sequoia National Park?" asked Bo.

2. "No, but I would like to see the giant sequoia trees that grow there, said Tuan.

3. I went there last summer during a trip to California," said Uri.

4. I learned that giant sequoias are named after Sequoya, a Cherokee, he added.

5. Uri also said that he met a helpful ranger at the park.

6. The ranger said that the General Sherman Tree is the largest tree in the world.

7. Uri explained, "The tree is about 275 feet tall and 83 feet around near its base."

8. Uri also said that the tree is about 3,500 years old.

9. "Sequoia National Park is the second oldest national park in the U.S., said Bo.

10. It's a good thing that the trees in the park are protected, said Tuan.

**Lesson 50** Add quotation marks and other punctuation marks to make each sentence correct.

1. The view from the top of this hill is beautiful said Jean.

2. I feel like an eagle flying over the city" she added.

3. "Wow, I can see the ocean and the mountains" exclaimed Tom.

4. I can see buildings, bridges, and many homes, remarked Nicole.

5. Look at all the cars on the freeway said Jean.

6. Do you see the boats sailing across the bay?" she asked.

7. "What was this place like before the city was built" he asked.

8. It was covered with grasses and shrubs, said Jean.

9. The hills were still very steep," added Nicole.

10. There were no tall buildings, cars, or freeways said Tom.

Name _____

Decide which group of words is a complete sentence. Fill in the letter that matches it.

1. (a) Visited a ghost town.

   (b) Marco and I visited a ghost town.

2. (a) The store had old jars and bottles on its shelves.

   (b) Old jars and bottles on its shelves.

3. (a) My grandfather visited Utah.

   (b) Swam in the Great Salt Lake.

4. (a) A postcard with a picture of a covered wagon.

   (b) The desert is beautiful in the spring.

Decide whether each underlined phrase is the subject or the predicate. Fill in the circle that matches it.

5. The Aztec people carved statues from stone.        (a) subject  (b) predicate

6. They decorated some statues with colored stones.   (a) subject  (b) predicate

7. They made capes out of feathers.                   (a) subject  (b) predicate

8. Some Hopi people built pueblos with mud bricks.    (a) subject  (b) predicate

9. These buildings stay cool in the summer.           (a) subject  (b) predicate

Decide which underlined group is the prepositional phrase. Fill in the circle that matches it. (Remember that a prepositional phrase tells *how, when, where,* or *how much.*)

10. The five clowns ran into the ring.        (a)        (b)
       a            b

11. The tallest one waved at my sister.       (a)        (b)
       a            b

12. A wire walker balanced above our heads.   (a)        (b)
       a                    b

13. A large net hung below the wire.          (a)        (b)
       a            b

Name _____

**Choose the sentence in each pair that has correct punctuation. Fill in the matching letter.**

14. (a) I went to a movie it was about New Orleans.

(b) I went to a movie. It was about New Orleans.

15. (a) New Orleans is a beautiful city. My aunt lives there.

(b) New Orleans is a beautiful city, my aunt lives there.

16. (a) The music in New Orleans is lively the food is spicy.

(b) The music in New Orleans is lively, and the food is spicy.

17. (a) You can fly there, or you can drive across a bridge.

(b) You can fly there you can drive across a bridge.

**Decide which is the best end mark for each sentence. Fill in the circle with the letter that matches it.**

18. Where is my social studies book          (a) !     (b) ?     (c) .

19. I have to read the chapter about New York City     (a) !     (b) ?     (c) .

20. Your dog is chewing up my book          (a) !     (b) ?     (c) .

21. Pass me the roll of tape          (a) !     (b) ?     (c) .

22. Do you think my teacher will notice          (a) !     (b) ?     (c) .

**Decide which sentence gives more information. Fill in the circle that matches it.**

23. (a) Baltimore is big.

(b) Baltimore is the largest city in the state of Maryland.

24. (a) Francis Scott Key wrote "The Star Spangled Banner" on a ship in Baltimore's harbor.

(b) A famous song was written in Baltimore.

25. (a) The song became the national anthem of the United States in 1931.

(b) It is an important song now.

Decide which underlined word is a noun. Fill in the circle with the letter that matches it.

1.  Look at <u>this</u> <u>picture</u>.
           a    b
               ⓐ       ⓑ

2.  It was <u>taken</u> on my <u>birthday</u>.
           a        b
               ⓐ       ⓑ

Decide which underlined word is a proper noun. Fill in the circle with the letter that matches it.

3.  I was getting on a <u>train</u> with <u>Uncle Trevor</u>.
             a       b
             ⓐ       ⓑ

4.  We were taking a <u>trip</u> to <u>Chicago</u>.
           a   b
             ⓐ       ⓑ

5.  We started our <u>journey</u> in <u>Cleveland</u>.
           a    b
             ⓐ       ⓑ

Choose the correct pronoun to replace each underlined word or phrase. Fill in the circle next to your answer.

6.  <u>Uncle Trevor</u> plays the piano.
    ⓐ She    ⓑ He    ⓒ They    ⓓ We

7.  <u>My aunt and I</u> like to sing along.
    ⓐ They    ⓑ You    ⓒ She    ⓓ We

8.  <u>My aunt and uncle</u> are a lot of fun.
    ⓐ They    ⓑ You    ⓒ She    ⓓ We

9.  <u>The violin in my hands</u> is very old.
    ⓐ That    ⓑ Those    ⓒ This    ⓓ These

10. <u>The drums in the corner</u> belong to my dad.
    ⓐ That    ⓑ Those    ⓒ This    ⓓ These

**Fill in the circle next to the word that correctly completes each sentence.**

11. I got two ____ for my birthday.    (a) books   (b) book

12. Both of my ____ have read the books before.    (a) brother   (b) brothers

13. The books ____ gifts from my grandparents.    (a) was    (b) were

14. I ____ happy to get them.    (a) was    (b) were

15. One book ____ full of fairy tales.    (a) are    (b) is

16. The stories ____ very old.    (a) are    (b) is

17. "Snow White" ____ "Hansel and Gretel" are my favorites.
   (a) but      (b) and

18. I like stories with happy endings, ____ my brothers prefer scary stories.
   (a) but      (b) or

19. Two brothers named Grimm ____ these fairy tales long ago.
   (a) collect   (b) collected

20. The Grimm brothers ____ in Germany in the 1800s.
   (a) live      (b) lived

**Decide which underlined word is a verb. Fill in the circle with the matching letter.**

21. Villagers and farmers <u>told</u> the Grimm <u>brothers</u> hundreds of stories.
                     (a)                (b)

22. The brothers <u>collected</u> stories from many nearby <u>villages</u>.
             (a)                   (b)

23. The Grimm brothers <u>wrote</u> 156 <u>stories</u> in all.
             (a)      (b)

**Decide which underlined word is an adjective. Fill in the circle with the matching letter.**

24. Many of the stories the Grimm <u>brothers</u> wrote had <u>scary</u> endings.
                    (a)               (b)

25. <u>Modern</u> writers have <u>changed</u> some of these endings.
    (a)           (b)

**Find the correct word to complete each sentence. Fill in the circle next to that word.**

1. Are you wearing _____ lucky sneakers?
   - (a) your
   - (b) you're

2. _____ going to jump high in them.
   - (a) Your
   - (b) You're

3. Did you practice _____ jump shot?
   - (a) your
   - (b) you're

4. The fans will sit over _____.
   - (a) their
   - (b) there

5. _____ going to cheer for both teams.
   - (a) Their
   - (b) They're

6. Some Bobcat fans painted whiskers on _____ faces.
   - (a) their
   - (b) there

7. _____ team colors are yellow and red.
   - (a) They're
   - (b) Their

8. _____ almost time to go.
   - (a) Its
   - (b) It's

9. Please put the bird back in _____ cage.
   - (a) its
   - (b) it's

10. _____ tidier that way.
    - (a) Its
    - (b) It's

11. My sister is _____ expert chess player.
    - (a) a
    - (b) an

12. It can take _____ long time to finish a chess match.
    - (a) a
    - (b) an

13. Kristin likes chess _____ than checkers.
    - (a) better
    - (b) gooder

14. I am a _____ chess player than Kristin.
    - (a) worser
    - (b) worse

**Decide which word belongs in each sentence. Fill in the circle next to your answer.**

15. My sister and I _____ outside yesterday to play horseshoes.
    - (a) gone
    - (b) go
    - (c) went

16. The horseshoes had _____ from the hooves of horses.
    - (a) came
    - (b) come
    - (c) comes

17. It's not easy to find _____ horseshoes these days.
    - (a) very
    - (b) real

18. Horseshoes made of wood work _____ well.
    - (a) very
    - (b) real

19. My sister _____ the first turn.
    - (a) take
    - (b) taken
    - (c) took

20. I _____ her a high five when her horseshoe looped around the stake.
    - (a) gave
    - (b) given
    - (c) gives

21. The horseshoe _____ as it hit the stake.
    - (a) ringed
    - (b) rang
    - (c) ring

22. My sister _____ a little song in celebration.
    - (a) singed
    - (b) sung
    - (c) sang

23. She looked so funny that I wished I had _____ my camera.
    - (a) bringed
    - (b) brought
    - (c) brung

24. We _____ at my grandmother's house last night.
    - (a) sleeped
    - (b) slept
    - (c) sleep

25. This morning we _____ pancakes for breakfast.
    - (a) ate
    - (b) aten
    - (c) eaten

**Decide which underlined word is not needed in each sentence. Fill in the circle with the letter that matches it.**

1. The <u>elk</u> <u>they</u> ran swiftly.
    a   b
           (a)      (b)

2. The wolves <u>they</u> <u>could</u> not catch them.
        a   b
           (a)      (b)

3. There is <u>not</u> <u>no</u> reason to be afraid of moths.
        a  b
           (a)      (b)

4. Moths <u>never</u> bite <u>no</u> people.
    a      b
           (a)      (b)

**Choose the correct pronoun to replace each word or phrase in bold type. Fill in the circle next to your answer.**

5. **Wolves** rarely live alone.
    (a) It    (b) She    (c) We    (d) They

6. **James** heard wolves howling in the hills.
    (a) He    (b) It    (c) She    (d) They

7. Miguel gave a book about birds to **Miriam**.
    (a) us    (b) I    (c) her    (d) them

8. I brought **a feather** to school.
    (a) you    (b) him    (c) it    (d) us

9. Our teacher showed **our class** a film about owls.
    (a) him    (b) us    (c) it    (d) her

10. **Lois and I** went to the zoo.
    (a) We    (b) Us    (c) She    (d) Them

11. **Angela and Kim** liked the young tiger cubs.
    (a) She    (b) Them    (c) They    (d) Us

12. Ira met **Molly and me** by the bird cages.
    (a) she    (b) we    (c) us    (d) them

**Name** _____

**Choose the correct word or phrase to complete each sentence. Fill in the circle next to that word or phrase.**

13. _____ found a snake in the backyard.
    (a) José and me    (b) José and I

14. The snake hissed at _____.
    (a) José and me    (b) me and José

15. Jean's dog _____ its tail when it sees me.
    (a) wag    (b) wags

16. The neighbor's dogs _____ all night.
    (a) bark    (b) barks

17. My dog _____ to the park with me.
    (a) run    (b) runs

18. This morning those goats _____ very hungry.
    (a) was    (b) were

19. Now they _____ asleep in the barn.
    (a) are    (b) is

20. The reddish-brown goat _____ my favorite.
    (a) is    (b) are

21. Yesterday Jeremy _____ the hamsters' cage.
    (a) cleans    (b) cleaned

22. Last week the hamsters _____ out of their cage.
    (a) crawl    (b) crawled

23. Now he always _____ the cage door.
    (a) closed    (b) closes

24. The blue whale is the _____ mammal on Earth.
    (a) most large    (b) larger    (c) largest

25. The blue whale is much _____ than an elephant.
    (a) biggest    (b) bigger    (c) more big

**Decide which word should be capitalized. Fill in the circle with the matching letter.**

1. **rain** falls **from** the clouds.       ⓐ    ⓑ
    a      b

2. **where** is my **umbrella?**       ⓐ    ⓑ
    a        b

3. My **friend carlo** is a weather forecaster.       ⓐ    ⓑ
      a   b

4. He **predicts** the weather in **colorado.**       ⓐ    ⓑ
      a          b

5. <u>The Darkest **cloud**</u> is a **very** good book.       ⓐ    ⓑ
         a     b

6. I read a **book called** <u>Weather **prediction** Made Easy</u>.       ⓐ    ⓑ
      a              b

**Decide where the comma belongs in each sentence. Fill in the circle with the matching letter.**

7. Plants, animals_ and people_ need the sun to survive.       ⓐ    ⓑ
         a       b

8. The sunshine made_ roses_ lilies, and daisies bloom.       ⓐ    ⓑ
         a   b

9. Yes_ it is hard_ to see in the fog.       ⓐ    ⓑ
     a     b

10. No_ fog is not really as thick_ as pea soup.       ⓐ    ⓑ
     a        b

**Decide where quotation marks belong in each sentence. Fill in the circle with the matching letter.**

11. "We want to play in the rain,_ said Margo and Lucy._       ⓐ    ⓑ
               a        b

12. Their mother _ said, _Wear your boots."       ⓐ    ⓑ
         a   b

13. "Hey, you splashed me!_ Margo yelled_.       ⓐ    ⓑ
        a     b

**Name** _____    

**Choose the right way to shorten the underlined part of the sentence. Fill in the circle next to your answer.**

14. The storm blew a tree down on Perry <u>Street</u>.
    ⓐ st  　　　　　ⓑ St.

15. <u>Doctor</u> Wong told us the winds were very strong.
    ⓐ Dr.  　　　　ⓑ DR.

16. <u>Benjamin</u> Franklin flew a kite in a storm.
    ⓐ B.  　　　　ⓑ B

17. <u>A book Kira bought</u> tells about hurricanes.
    ⓐ Kiras book  　　ⓑ Kira's book

18. <u>The center of a hurricane</u> is called the *eye*.
    ⓐ A hurricane's center  　ⓑ A hurricanes' center

19. We took shelter in <u>a house owned by my cousins</u>.
    ⓐ my cousins' house  　ⓑ my cousins's house

20. <u>I have</u> never seen a tornado.
    ⓐ Ive  　　　　ⓑ I've

21. I <u>would not</u> want to be caught in one.
    ⓐ wouldn't  　　ⓑ would'nt

22. <u>They are</u> violent funnel-shaped storms.
    ⓐ Theyr'e  　　ⓑ They're

**Decide which sentence has correct punctuation. Fill in the circle next to your answer.**

23. ⓐ Renee asked, "What are clouds made of?
    ⓑ Renee asked, "What are clouds made of?"

24. ⓐ "Water vapor forms clouds." the scientist answered.
    ⓑ "Water vapor forms clouds," the scientist answered.

25. ⓐ Renee said, "That must be why clouds make rain."
    ⓑ Renee said "That must be why clouds make rain."

# Grammar, Usage, and Mechanics Handbook
## Table of Contents

## Mechanics

## Sentence Structure and Parts of Speech

## Usage

## Letters and E-mails

## Research

## Guidelines for Listening and Speaking

Name _____

# Mechanics

## Section 1 Capitalization

- **Capitalize the first word in a sentence.**

  <u>T</u>he kangaroo rat is an amazing animal.

- **Capitalize people's names and the names of particular places.**

  <u>G</u>regory <u>G</u>ordon          <u>W</u>ashington <u>M</u>onument

- **Capitalize titles of respect.**

  <u>M</u>r. Alvarez          <u>D</u>r. Chin          <u>M</u>s. Murphy

- **Capitalize family titles used just before people's names and titles that are part of names.**

  <u>U</u>ncle Frank          <u>A</u>unt Mary          <u>G</u>overnor Adamson

- **Capitalize initials of names.**

  Thomas Paul Gerard (<u>T</u>.<u>P</u>. Gerard)

- **Capitalize place names and words formed from them.**

  <u>F</u>rance          <u>F</u>rench          <u>C</u>hina          <u>C</u>hinese

- **Capitalize the months of the year and the days of the week.**

  <u>F</u>ebruary          <u>A</u>pril          <u>M</u>onday          <u>T</u>uesday

- **Capitalize important words in the names of groups.**

  <u>A</u>merican <u>L</u>ung <u>A</u>ssociation          <u>V</u>eterans of <u>F</u>oreign <u>W</u>ars

- **Capitalize important words in the names of holidays.**

  <u>V</u>eterans <u>D</u>ay          <u>F</u>ourth of <u>J</u>uly

- **Capitalize the first word in the greeting or closing of a letter.**

  <u>D</u>ear Edmundo,          <u>Y</u>ours truly,

- **Capitalize the word *I*.**

  Frances and <u>I</u> watched the movie together.

- **Capitalize the first, last, and most important words in a title.**

  *Island of the Blue Dolphins*

- **Capitalize the first word in a direct quotation.**

  Aunt Rose said, "<u>P</u>lease pass the clam dip."

## Section 2 Abbreviations and Initials

*Abbreviations* are shortened forms of words. Many abbreviations begin with a capital letter and end with a period.

- **You can abbreviate titles of address.**

  Mister (Mr. Brian Davis)          Mistress (Mrs. Maria Rosario)
  Doctor (Dr. Emily Chu)            Junior (Everett Castle, Jr.)
  Note: *Ms.* is a title of address used for women. It is not an abbreviation, but it requires a period (Ms. Anita Brown).

- **You can abbreviate words used in addresses.**

  Street (St.)          Avenue (Ave.)          Route (Rte.)
  Boulevard (Blvd.)     Road (Rd.)

- **You can abbreviate days of the week.**

  Sunday (Sun.)         Wednesday (Wed.)       Friday (Fri.)
  Monday (Mon.)         Thursday (Thurs.)      Saturday (Sat.)
  Tuesday (Tues.)

- **You can abbreviate months of the year.**

  January (Jan.)        April (Apr.)           October (Oct.)
  February (Feb.)       August (Aug.)          November (Nov.)
  March (Mar.)          September (Sept.)      December (Dec.)
  (May, June, and July do not have abbreviated forms.)

- **You can abbreviate directions.**

  North (N)       East (E)       South (S)       West (W)

An *initial* is the first letter of a name. An initial is written as a capital letter and a period. Sometimes initials are used for the names of countries or cities.

  Michael Paul Sanders (M.P. Sanders)  United States of America (U.S.A.)
  Washington, District of Columbia (Washington, D.C.)

## Section 3 Titles

- **Underline titles of books, newspapers, TV series, movies, and magazines.**
  Island of the Blue Dolphins        Miami Herald          I Love Lucy
  Note: These titles are put in italics when using a word processor.

- **Use quotation marks around articles in magazines, short stories, chapters in books, songs, and poems.**
  "This Land Is Your Land"         "The Gift"          "Eletelephony"

- **Capitalize the first, last, and most important words.**
  *A Knight in the Attic*          *My Brother Sam Is Dead*
  Note: Capitalize the word *is* because it is a verb.

## Section 4  Quotation Marks

- Put quotation marks (" ") around the titles of articles, magazines, short stories, book chapters, songs, and poems.

  My favorite short story is "Revenge of the Reptiles."

- Put quotation marks around a *direct quotation,* or a speaker's exact words.

  "Did you see that alligator?" Max asked.

---

### Writing a Conversation

- Quotation marks are used to separate a speaker's exact words from the rest of the sentence. Begin a direct quotation with a capital letter.
  Use a comma to separate the direct quotation from the speaker's name.
  Rory said, "There are no alligators in this area."

- When a direct quotation comes at the end of a sentence, put the end mark inside the last quotation mark.
  Max cried, "Look out!"

- When writing a conversation, begin a new paragraph with each change of speaker.
  Rory and Max leaped away from the pond. Max panted, "I swear I saw a huge, scaly tail and a flat snout in the water!"
  "Relax," Rory said. "I told you there are no alligators around here."

---

## Section 5  Spelling

Use these tips if you are not sure how to spell a word you want to write:

- Think of a word you know that rhymes with the word you want to spell. Or think of a word you know that has parts that sound like the word you're spelling. Word parts that sound alike are often spelled the same.
  *Spell* rhymes with *well.*
  If you can spell *cat* and *log*, you can spell *catalog*.

- Say the word aloud and break it into parts, or syllables. Try spelling each word part. Put the parts together to spell the whole word.

- Write the word. Make sure there is a vowel in every syllable. If the word looks wrong to you, try spelling it other ways.

Correct spelling helps readers understand what you write. Use a dictionary to check the spellings of any words you are not sure about.

## Section 6  End Marks

Every sentence must end with a period, an exclamation point, or a question mark.

- Use a *period* at the end of a statement or a command.
  My grandfather and I look alike. (*statement*)
  Step back very slowly. (*command*)

- Use an *exclamation point* at the end of a firm command or at the end of a sentence that shows great feeling or excitement.
  Get away from the cliff! (*command*)
  What an incredible sight! (*exclamation*)

- Use a *question mark* at the end of an asking sentence.
  How many miles is it to Tucson? (*question*)

## Section 7  Apostrophes

An apostrophe (') is used to form the possessive of a noun or to join two words in a contraction.

- Possessives show ownership. To make a singular noun into a possessive, add an apostrophe and *s.*
  The bike belongs to Carmen. It is Carmen's bike.
  The truck belongs to Mr. Ross. It is Mr. Ross's truck.

- To form a possessive from a plural noun that ends in *s,* add only an apostrophe.
  Those books belong to my sisters. They are my sisters' books.
  Two families own this house. It is the families' vacation spot.

- Some plural nouns do not end in *s.* To form possessives with these nouns, add an apostrophe and *s.*
  The women own those boats. They are the women's boats.
  The children left their boots here. The children's boots are wet.

- Use an apostrophe to replace the dropped letters in a contraction.
  couldn't (could n<u>o</u>t)      it's (it <u>is</u>)
  didn't (did n<u>o</u>t)          I'm (I <u>am</u>)
  hasn't (has n<u>o</u>t)          they'll (they <u>wi</u>ll)

## Commas in Sentences

- **Use a comma after an introductory word in a sentence.**
  Yes, I'd love to go to the movies.
  Actually, we had a great time.

- **Use a comma to separate items in a series.**
  We ate cheese, bread, and fruit.
  The puppy whined, scratched at the door, and then barked loudly.

- **Use a comma when speaking directly to a person.**
  Akila, will you please stand up?
  We would like you to sing, Akila.

- **Use a comma to separate a direct quotation from the speaker's name.**
  Harold asked, "How long do I have to sit here?"
  "You must sit there until Anton returns," Vic said.

- **Use a comma with the joining words *and, or,* or *but* when combining two sentences.**
  Lisa liked the reptiles best, but Lyle preferred the amphibians.

## Commas in Letters

- **Use a comma after the greeting and closing of a friendly letter.**
  Dear Reginald,            Your friend, Deke

## Commas with Dates and Place Names

- **Use a comma to separate the month and the day from the year.**
  We clinched the division championship on September 20, 2008.

- **Use a comma to separate the day from the date.**
  It was Sunday, November 5.

- **Use a comma to separate the name of a city or town from the name of a state.**
  I visited Memphis, Tennessee.

# Sentence Structure and Parts of Speech

## Section 9 The Sentence

A *sentence* is a group of words that tells a complete thought. A sentence has two parts: a *subject* and a *predicate*.

- The subject tells *whom* or *what* the sentence is about.
  The swimmers race.

- The predicate tells what the subject *is* or *does*.
  The judge watches carefully.

There are four kinds of sentences: *statement, question, command,* and *exclamation.*

- A sentence that tells something is called a *telling sentence* or *statement.* It is also called a *declarative sentence.* A statement ends with a period.
  Jake swam faster than anyone.

- A sentence that asks something is called an *asking sentence* or *question.* It is also called an *interrogative sentence.* A question ends with a question mark.
  Did Sammy qualify for the finals?

- A sentence that tells someone to do something is called a *command.* It is also called an *imperative sentence.* A command usually ends with a period, but a firm command can end with an exclamation point.
  Keep your eyes on the finish line.
  Watch out for that bee!

- A sentence that shows excitement or surprise is called an *exclamation.* An exclamation ends with an exclamation point.
  Jake has won the race!

## Section 10 Subjects

The *subject* of a sentence tells whom or what the sentence is about.

- A sentence can have one subject.
  Mary wrote a book.

- A sentence can have more than one subject.
  Alex and Mark have already read the book.

## Section 11 Predicates

The *predicate* of a sentence tells what happened.

- A predicate can tell what the subject of the sentence did. This kind of predicate includes an action verb.

  Mary <u>won an award</u>.

- A predicate can also tell more about the subject. This kind of predicate includes a linking verb.

  Mary <u>is a talented writer</u>.

A *compound predicate* is two or more predicates that share the same subject. Compound predicates are often connected by the joining word *and* or *or*.

  Ramon <u>sang and danced</u> in the play.  Mary <u>wrote the play and directed it</u>.

## Section 12 Fragments and Run-on Sentences

A *fragment* is not a sentence, because it is missing a subject or a predicate.

- Fragments are also called *incomplete sentences* because they do not tell a complete thought.

  Sumi and Ali. (*missing a predicate that tells what happened*)

  Went hiking in the woods. (*missing a subject that tells who*)

A *run-on sentence* is two complete sentences that are run together.

  Sumi went hiking Ali went swimming.

- To fix a run-on sentence, use a comma and *and, or,* or *but* to join the two complete sentences.

  Sumi went hiking<u>, but</u> Ali went swimming.

Try not to string too many short sentences together when you write. Instead, combine sentences and take out unnecessary information.

  **Incorrect:** I stared at him and he stared at me and I told him to go away and he wouldn't so then I called my big sister.

  **Correct:** We stared at each other. I told him to go away, but he wouldn't. Then I called my big sister.

## Section 13 Nouns

A *common noun* names a person, place, or thing.

  Ira visited an auto <u>museum</u> with his <u>friends</u>. They saw old <u>cars</u> there.

A *proper noun* names a certain person, place, or thing. Proper nouns begin with a capital letter.

  <u>Ira</u> wants to visit the <u>Sonoran Desert</u> in <u>Mexico</u>.

## Section 14 Adjectives

An *adjective* is a word that tells more about a noun.

- Some adjectives tell what kind.
  Jim observed the <u>huge</u> elephant. The <u>enormous</u> beast towered above him.

- Some adjectives tell how many.
  The elephant was <u>twelve</u> feet tall. It weighed <u>several</u> tons.

- Sometimes an adjective follows the noun it describes.
  Jim was <u>careful</u> not to anger the elephant. The elephant was <u>frightening</u>.

- *A, an,* and *the* are articles, a special kind of adjective. Use *a* before a singular noun that begins with a consonant sound. Use *an* before a singular noun that begins with a vowel sound.
  <u>A</u> rhino is not as heavy as <u>an</u> elephant.

## Section 15 Pronouns

A *pronoun* can replace a noun naming a person, place, and thing. Pronouns include *I, me, you, we, us, he, she, it, they,* and *them.*

- A pronoun may take the place of the subject of a sentence. Do not use both the pronoun and the noun it replaces together.
  **Incorrect:** <u>Rita she</u> made the team.
  **Correct:** Rita plays goalie. <u>She</u> never lets the other team score.

- A pronoun may replace a noun that is the direct object of a verb.
  Rita's team played the Bobcats. Rita's team beat <u>them</u>.

- A pronoun must match the noun it replaces. A singular pronoun must be used in place of a singular noun. A plural pronoun must be used in place of a plural noun.
  <u>Nick</u> saved the game. <u>He</u> kicked a goal at the last minute.
  <u>The Bobcats</u> were upset. <u>They</u> had not lost a game all season.

- *This, that, these,* and *those* can be used as demonstrative pronouns. Use *this* and *these* to talk about one or more things that are nearby. Use *that* and *those* to talk about one or more things that are far away.
  <u>This</u> is a soft rug.
  <u>These</u> are sweeter than those over there.
  <u>That</u> is where I sat yesterday.
  <u>Those</u> are new chairs.

- Possessive pronouns show ownership. The words *my, your, his, her, its, their,* and *our* are possessive pronouns.
  Those skates belong to my brother. Those are <u>his</u> kneepads, too.

## Section 16 Verbs

An *action verb* shows action in a sentence.

> Scientists <u>study</u> the natural world.
> They <u>learn</u> how the laws of nature work.

- Sometimes a *helping verb* is needed to help the main verb show action. A helping verb comes before a main verb.

  Some scientists <u>are</u> studying the glaciers of Antarctica.
  These studies <u>will</u> help scientists learn about Earth's history.

- Verbs can tell about the *present*, the *past*, or the *future*.

  Few people <u>travel</u> in Antarctica. (*present tense*)
  Explorers first <u>traveled</u> to the South Pole over 100 years ago. (*past tense*)
  Other explorers <u>will travel</u> to the South Pole in the future. (*future tense*)

- To show past action, *-ed* is added to most verbs. Verbs that do not add *-ed* are called *irregular verbs*. Here are some common irregular verbs.

| Present | Past | With *have, has,* or *had* |
|---------|------|---------------------------|
| bring | brought | brought |
| come | came | come |
| eat | ate | eaten |
| give | gave | given |
| go | went | gone |
| ring | rang | rung |
| sing | sang | sung |
| sleep | slept | slept |
| take | took | taken |

- The subject and its verb must agree. Add *s* or *es* to a verb in the present tense when the subject is a singular noun or *he, she,* or *it.* Do not add *s* if the subject is a plural noun or if the subject is *I, you, we,* or *they.*

  An Antarctic explorer needs special equipment.
  (*singular subject:* **An Antarctic explorer;** *verb + s or es:* **needs**)
  Explorers carry climbing tools and survival gear.
  (*plural subject:* **Explorers;** *verb without s or es:* **carry**)
  I like stories about Antarctica.
  (*subject:* **I;** *verb without s or es:* **like**)

A *linking verb* does not show action. It connects the subject of a sentence to a word or words in the predicate that tell about the subject. Linking verbs include *am, is, are, was,* and *were. Seem* and *become* are linking verbs, too.

> Explorers <u>are</u> brave. That route <u>seems</u> very long and dangerous.

**Note:** *Feel, taste, smell, sound,* and *look* can be action or linking verbs.

## Section 17 Adverbs

An *adverb* is usually used to describe a verb.

- **Many adverbs end in -*ly*.**
  Andrew approached the snake cage <u>slowly</u>. He <u>cautiously</u> peered inside.

- **Some adverbs do not end in -*ly*.**
  Andrew knew that snakes can move <u>fast</u>.

- ***Very*** **is an adverb meaning "to a high degree" or "extremely." Never use**
  *real* **in place of** *very*.
  Incorrect: The snake's fangs were <u>real</u> sharp.
  Correct: The snake's fangs were <u>very</u> sharp.

## Section 18 Prepositions

A *preposition* helps tell *when, where,* or *how.*

- **Prepositions include the words** *on, in, at, under,* **and** *over.*
  Jeff left the milk <u>on</u> the table.
  He knew it belonged <u>in</u> the refrigerator.

- **A** *prepositional phrase* **is a group of words that includes a preposition and its object. In the sentence below,** *in* **is the preposition and** *minutes* **is the object of the preposition.**
  Jeff knew his mother would be home <u>in five minutes</u>.

## Section 19 Conjunctions

The words *and, or,* and *but* are *conjunctions.*

- **Conjunctions may be used to join words within a sentence.**
  My favorite reptiles are snakes <u>and</u> lizards.
  Najim doesn't like snakes <u>or</u> lizards.
  He thinks reptiles are cute <u>but</u> dumb.

- **Conjunctions can be used to join two or more sentences. When using a conjunction to join sentences, put a comma before the conjunction. (The conjunction** *and* **does not need a comma if both sentences are short.)**
  I like amphibians, <u>but</u> Najim thinks they are creepy.
  We could visit a snake farm next, <u>or</u> we could go somewhere else.
  I waited <u>and</u> I waited.

# Usage

## Section 20 Negatives

A *negative word* says "no" or "not."

- Often negatives are in the form of contractions.
  
  Do **not** enter that room.          **Don't** even go near the door.

- In most sentences it is not correct to use two negatives.

| Incorrect | Correct |
|---|---|
| We **can't** see **nothing**. | We **can't** see anything. |
| We **haven't** got **no** solution. | We **haven't** got a solution. |

## Section 21 Comparisons

- To compare two people, places, or things, add *-er* to most adjectives and adverbs.
  
  An elephant is **tall**. A giraffe is **taller**.
  
  A lion runs **fast**. A cheetah runs **faster**.

- To compare three or more items, add *-est* to most adjectives and adverbs.
  
  The giraffe is the **tallest** land animal.
  
  The cheetah is the **fastest** of any animal on land.

- When comparing two or more things using the ending *-er* or *-est,* never use the word *more*.

| Incorrect | Correct |
|---|---|
| She is **more faster** than he is. | She is **faster** than he is. |

- The words *more* and *most* can also be used to compare two or more persons, places, or things.
  
  Mario is **excited** about the field trip.
  
  Duane is **more excited** than Mario.
  
  Kiki is the **most excited** student of all.

- Sometimes the words *good* and *bad* are used to compare. These words change forms in comparisons.

| | |
|---|---|
| Mario is a **good** athlete. | The basketball court is in **bad** shape. |
| Kiki is a **better** athlete. | The tennis court is in **worse** shape than the basketball court. |
| Bill is the **best** athlete of all. | The ice rink is in the **worst** shape of all. |

  Note: Use *better* or *worse* to compare two things. Use *best* or *worst* to compare three or more things.

## Section 22 Contractions

When two or more words are combined to form one word, one or more letters are dropped and replaced by an apostrophe. These words are called *contractions*.

- In the contraction below, an apostrophe takes the place of the letters *wi*.
  he will = he'll

- Here are some other contractions.

  cannot/can't          have not/haven't          they have/they've
  could not/couldn't    he would/he'd             they will/they'll
  did not/didn't        I will/I'll               they would/they'd
  do not/don't          it is/it's                we are/we're
  does not/doesn't      she will/she'll
  has not/hasn't        they are/they're

## Section 23 Plural Nouns

- A *singular noun* names one person, place, or thing.
  girl          pond          arrow          donkey

- A *plural noun* names more than one person, place, or thing. To make most singular nouns plural, add *s*.
  girls          ponds          arrows          donkeys

- For nouns ending in *sh, ch, x,* or *z*, add *es* to make the word plural.
  bush/bushes          box/boxes
  lunch/lunches        quiz/quizzes

- For nouns ending in a consonant and *y*, change the *y* to *i* and add *es*.
  penny/pennies          army/armies

- For nouns that end in *f* or *fe*, replace *f* or *fe* with *ves* to make the noun plural.
  shelf/shelves          wife/wives

- Some words change spelling when the plural is formed.
  man/men     woman/women     mouse/mice     goose/geese

- Some words have the same singular and plural form.
  deer          sheep

## Section 24 Possessive Nouns

A *possessive noun* shows ownership.

- **To make a singular noun possessive, add an apostrophe and s.**
  John<u>'s</u> bat                    the girl<u>'s</u> bike

- **When a singular noun ends in s, add an apostrophe and s.**
  Ross<u>'s</u> project                James<u>'s</u> glasses

- **To make a plural noun possessive, add an apostrophe.**
  the soldiers<u>'</u> songs           the girls<u>'</u> bikes

- **When a plural noun does not end in s, add an apostrophe and s.**
  the men<u>'s</u> ideas               the children<u>'s</u> shoes

## Section 25 Problem Words

These words are often misused in writing.

| | |
|---|---|
| sit | *Sit* means "rest or stay in one place." <br> Sit down and relax for a while. |
| sat | *Sat* is the past tense of sit. <br> I sat in that chair yesterday. |
| set | *Set* is a verb meaning "put." <br> Set the chair here. |

|  |  |
|---|---|
|  | *A, an,* and *the* are articles. |
| a | *A* is usually used before a singular noun beginning with a consonant. <br> a wagon                a bicycle                a ruler |
| an | *An* is usually used before a singular noun that begins with a vowel. <br> an article              an igloo                an orangutan |
| the | *The* is used before a singular or plural noun. <br> the ocean               the birds               the people |

| | |
|---|---|
| may | *May* is used to ask permission or to express a possibility. <br> May I have another hot dog?        I may borrow that book someday. |
| can | *Can* shows that someone is able to do something. <br> I can easily eat three hot dogs. |

| | |
|---|---|
| is | Use *is* to tell about one person, place, or thing. <br> Alabama is warm during the summer. |
| are | Use *are* to tell about more than one person, place, or thing. Also use *are* with the word *you*. <br> Seattle and San Francisco are cool during the summer. <br> You are welcome to visit me anytime. |

| | |
|---|---|
| **doesn't** | The contraction *doesn't* is used with the singular pronouns *he, she,* and *it*. |
| | He doesn't like sauerkraut.          It doesn't agree with him. |
| **don't** | The contraction *don't* is used with the plural pronouns *we* and *they*. *Don't* is also used with *I* and *you*. |
| | They don't like swiss cheese.          I don't care for it, either. |
| **I** | Use the pronoun *I* as the subject of a sentence. When using *I* with another noun or pronoun, always name yourself last. |
| | I am going to basketball camp.          Renée and I will ride together. |
| **me** | Use the pronoun *me* after action verbs. |
| | Renée will play me one-on-one. |
| | Also use *me* after a preposition, such as *to, at,* and *with*. |
| | Pass the ball to me.          Come to the game with Renée and me. |
| **good** | *Good* is an adjective. |
| **well** | *Well* is an adverb. These words are often used incorrectly. |
| | **Incorrect:** Renée plays good. |
| | **Correct:** Renée plays well. She is a good basketball player. |
| **let** | *Let* is a verb that means "allow." |
| | Please let me go to the mall with you. |
| **leave** | *Leave* is a verb that means "go away from" or "let stay." |
| | We will leave at noon.          Leave your sweater here. |
| **was** | *Was* is a past tense form of the verb *be*. Use *was* to tell about one person or thing. |
| | Hana was sad yesterday. |
| **were** | *Were* is also a past tense form of *be*. Use *were* to tell about more than one person or thing. |
| | Hana and her friend were both unhappy. |
| | Also use the word *were* with *you*. |
| | Were you home yesterday? |
| **has** | Use *has* to tell about one person or thing. |
| | Rory has a stamp collection. |
| **have** | Use *have* to tell about more than one. Also use *have* with the pronoun *I*. |
| | David and Lin have a rock collection. |
| | I have a bottle cap collection. |

## Section 26 Homophones

Some words sound alike but have different spellings and meanings. These words are called *homophones*. Here are some homophones that are often confused in writing.

| | |
|---|---|
| are | *Are* is a form of the verb *be*. |
| | We are best friends. |
| our | *Our* is a possessive pronoun. |
| | Our favorite color is green. |
| hour | An *hour* is sixty minutes. |
| | Meet me in an hour. |
| its | *Its* is a possessive pronoun. |
| | The horse shook its shaggy head. |
| it's | *It's* is a contraction of the words *it is*. |
| | It's a beautiful day for a ride. |
| there | *There* is an adverb that usually means "in that place." *There* is also used in the expressions "there is" and "there are." |
| | Please put the books there. |
| | There is a library nearby. |
| their | *Their* is a possessive pronoun. It shows something belongs to more than one person or thing. |
| | Their tickets are in my pocket. |
| they're | *They're* is a contraction made from the words *they are*. |
| | They're waiting for me inside. |
| two | *Two* is a number. |
| | Broccoli and cauliflower are two vegetables I like. |
| to | *To* means "toward." |
| | I brought the pot to the stove. |
| too | *Too* means "also." It can also mean "more than enough." |
| | I'd like some lunch, too. |
| | There is too much pepper in my soup. |
| your | *Your* is a possessive pronoun. |
| | Where are your socks? |
| you're | *You're* is a contraction made from the words *you are*. |
| | You're coming with us, aren't you? |

# Letters and E-mails

## Section 27 Letters

A *friendly letter* is an informal letter written to a friend or family member.

In a friendly letter, you might send a message, invite someone to a party, or thank someone for a gift. A friendly letter has five parts.

- The *heading* gives your address and the date.

- The *greeting* includes the name of the person you are writing to.

- The *main part* of the letter, or the *body*, gives your message.

- The *closing* is a friendly or polite way to say good-bye.

- The *signature* is your name.

A *business letter* is a formal letter.

You would write a business letter to a company, a newspaper, or any person you do not know well. A business letter looks a lot like a friendly letter, but a business letter includes the name and address of the business you are writing to, substitutes a colon for a comma after the greeting, omits paragraph indentations, and aligns all of the letter parts along the left-hand margin.

The envelope below shows how to address a letter. A friendly letter and a business letter are addressed the same way.

---

35 Rand Street
Chicago, IL 60606
July 15, 2012

Dear Kim,

  Hi from the big city. I'm spending the summer learning to skateboard. My brother Raj is teaching me. He's a pro.

  I have one skateboard and hope to buy another one soon. If I can do that, we can practice together when you come to visit.

  Your friend,
  *Art*

---

35 Rand Street
Chicago, IL  60606
July 15, 2012

Swenson Skateboard Company
10026 Portage Road
Lansing, MI  48091

Dear Sir or Madam:

Please send me your latest skateboard catalog. I am particularly interested in your newest models, the K-7 series.

Thank you.

Sincerely yours,
*Arthur Quinn*
Arthur Quinn

---

ARTHUR QUINN
35 RAND ST
CHICAGO IL  60606

  KIM LEE
  1555 MONTAGUE BLVD
  MEMPHIS TN  38106

## Section 28 E-mails

An *e-mail* is a note sent from one person to another person, a group, or a company through a computer network. Today, many people use e-mail to stay in touch with friends and family. An e-mail should contain five parts, like a letter does.

- An e-mail contains a *greeting*, a *body*, a *closing*, and your *name*.
- An e-mail *header* contains your e-mail address, the e-mail address of the person you are writing to, the date, and a subject line.

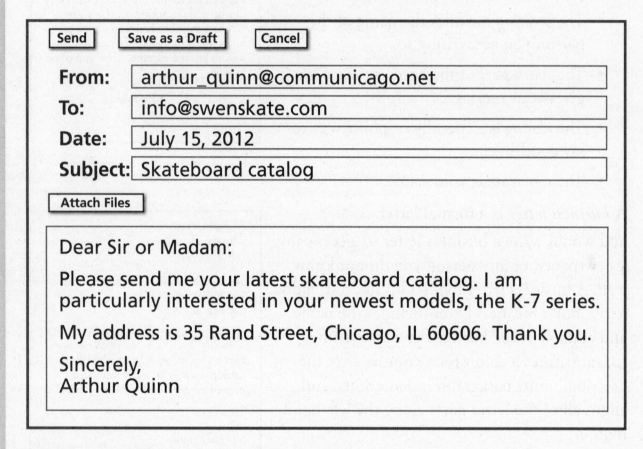

```
Send      Save as a Draft      Cancel

From:    arthur_quinn@communicago.net
To:      info@swenskate.com
Date:    July 15, 2012
Subject: Skateboard catalog

Attach Files
```

Dear Sir or Madam:

Please send me your latest skateboard catalog. I am particularly interested in your newest models, the K-7 series.

My address is 35 Rand Street, Chicago, IL 60606. Thank you.

Sincerely,
Arthur Quinn

# Research

## Section 29 Library Research

You can find information for a report or a project in a library.

- Many libraries have an information desk. The person at the desk can help you look for information.
- Libraries have many reference books, including dictionaries, thesauruses, and encyclopedias. You can use these to find information about words, and basic information about topics.

- Libraries have nonfiction books about all kinds of subjects. You can find books on a particular subject by entering that subject into a computer connected to the library's database. This database lists all the publications in the library. The computer will usually list several books on the subject you entered. Each listing will have a code that tells where in the library that book can be found.

## Section 30 Internet Research

**You can use online dictionaries, thesauruses, and encyclopedias to find basic information about words and topics. You can also find information for a report or a project by using an Internet *search engine*.**

- Think of **key words** that tell what you are looking for. For example, if you need information on animals that live in the rainforest, you might use the key words **rainforest animals**. Type these words into the search engine's text box.

- The search engine will give you links to **Web sites**. You can click on a link to visit a Web site.

- When you get to the Web site, you need to judge whether it will be a good source of information. One way to tell if a Web site is a reliable source is to look at who put up the site. When you see the name of a well-known institution, such as a museum or library, you can tell that the site will probably be a good source.

### Internet Safety

Be sure to follow safety rules whenever you use the Internet. These rules will help you keep personal information private.

- When you log on to a school computer, you may type your own name as a username. However, when you go on the Internet, you use a screen name. That should never be your real name or nickname. You will also use a password, a secret word or symbol that identifies who you are. Keep your password safe. Do not share it with anyone. Never use your address, birthday, phone number, or pet's name as a password. Those are too easy for someone else to figure out.

- Have you ever received e-mail with an attachment? Usually you must click the attachment to load it into your computer. Never download attachments from strangers. These may harm your computer.

# Guidelines for Listening and Speaking

## Section 31  Listening

These steps will help you be a good listener:

- **Listen carefully** when others are speaking.

- **Keep in mind your reason for listening.** Are you listening to learn about a topic? To be entertained? To get directions? Decide what you should get out of the listening experience.

- **Look directly at the speaker.** Doing this will help you concentrate on what he or she has to say.

- **Do not interrupt** the speaker or talk to others while the speaker is talking.

- **Ask questions** when the speaker is finished talking if there is anything you did not understand.

## Section 32  Speaking

Being a good speaker takes practice. These guidelines can help you become an effective speaker:

### Giving Oral Reports

- **Be prepared.** Know exactly what it is that you are going to talk about and how long you will speak. Have your notes in front of you.

- **Speak slowly** and **clearly.** Speak **loudly** enough so everyone can hear you.

- **Look** at your audience.

### Taking Part in Discussions

- **Listen** to what others have to say.

- **Disagree politely.** Let others in the group know you respect their point of view.

- **Try not to interrupt others.** Everyone should have a chance to speak.

# Topic Index

# Language Index